Healing in Psychotherapy
The Process of Holistic Change

PERSPECTIVES IN PSYCHOTHERAPY
A Series of Monographs

Edited by Paul Olsen for the National
Institute for the Psychotherapies

Volume 1

HEALING IN PSYCHOTHERAPY
The Process of Holistic Change

Diane Shainberg

This book is part of a series. The publisher will accept continuation orders which may be cancelled at any time and which provide for automatic billing and shipping of each title in the series upon publication. Please write for details.

Healing in Psychotherapy
The Process of Holistic Change

DIANE SHAINBERG
National Institute for the Psychotherapies

Gordon and Breach Science Publishers
Philadelphia   Reading   Paris   Montreux   Tokyo   Melbourne

Published 1983
Fourth Printing 1992

Gordon and Breach Science Publishers

5301 Tacony Street, Drawer 330
Philadelphia, Pennsylvania 19137
United States of America

Post Office Box 90
Reading, Berkshire RG1 8JL
United Kingdom

58, rue Lhomond
75005 Paris
France

3-14-9, Okubo
Shinjuku-ku, Tokyo 169
Japan

Private Bag 8
Camberwell, Victoria 3124
Australia

Library of Congress Cataloging in Publication Data

Shainberg, Diane, 1933–
    Healing in psychotherapy.

    (Perspectives in psychotherapy, ISSN 0735-4037 ; v. 1)
    1. Psychotherapy.   2. Holistic medicine.   I. Title.   II. Series. [DNLM:
1. Holistic health.   2. Psychotherapy.   W1 PE871G v.1 / WM 420 S526h]
RC480.5.S43 1983   616.89′14   82-24247
ISBN 0-677-06100-5 Hardcover
ISBN 0-677-21880-X Papercover

For Steven and Nancy

Contents

Preface to the Series

The major trends of the mental health profession are yet to be determined as we move on toward the middle of the 1980s. There are, however, some clues to the direction in which we are heading, the themes that are beginning to emerge. We may well see a growing emphasis on alienation, a sense on the part of the patient that he or she is "cut off" from others and from the environment as a whole — aspects of what Robert Jay Lifton has termed "the broken connection." Embedded in this vast matrix will be a profound experience of personal loneliness and a concomitant, perhaps desperate need to contact the psychotherapist on a deeper emotional level than many practitioners have ever before experienced. And psychotherapists may themselves not be immune to this sense, this feeling.

We may see, eventually, that this need is not rooted exclusively in psychopathology or developmental damage, but that it emanates from very palpable social factors. Thus there will be realignments in our theories of transference and countertransference, and a more intense focus on the "real" relationship between patient and therapist. The therapeutic encounter may have to become more interpersonally dynamic than we, as practitioners, have traditionally experienced or accepted.

At least that is how, in broad strokes, I view developments over the next several years. The work of the psychotherapist will become more difficult, more emotionally demanding, more theoretically wrenching.

A glimpse at the recent past:

The 1960s and early 1970s were marked by a literally bewildering array of therapeutic and quasitherapeutic modalities, a number of which achieved a peak of popularity, a kind of hey-day. Among them: Gestalt therapy, Primal Therapy, encounter groups, many offshoots of Bioenergetics, est, "body work" of all sorts, a variety of techniques aimed at directly stimulating affect. Jung's Analytic Psychology achieved a vigorous new popularity, buttressed certainly by the powerful emergence of Zen and Tibetan Buddhism, Yoga and Sufism. But, to paraphrase William Butler Yeats, the center did not hold. Things fell apart. And one might legitimately ask: Was there a center at all?

Side by side with these modalities and philosophical/religious systems (hypno-, group, and behavioral therapy did not founder) was the growing importance of Heinz Kohut's self-psychology and the development and greater sophistication of Object-Relations theory. These are of course psychoanalytic movements of great power and meaning — and they are at root interpersonally oriented. There can be no question of that, and what they have provided is a theoretical rationale for meaningful patient-therapist contact *in* the analytic session. The session becomes structured upon empathy, upon conscious and unconscious communication; detachment is no longer truly possible. Here obsolescence is not readily apparent; things do not appear to be falling apart.

Yet even more will be required, and we can only hope that these theoretical "schools" will continue to develop; I detect in them a strong underlying current of demystification and a real attempt to make contact with patients who live in this time, this era.

Only the passage of time will give us insights into what we have learned from all the disappearing modalities, into what we have learned from a decade of focus upon narcissism and the borderline character. Have we developed some tools to help us make deeper contact with our patients? Has the impact of the last two decades opened us somewhat more, emotionally? We tend to relegate obsolete things either to the trash heap or to the basement; in the latter case we may one day discover that we own a valuable antique. We must examine, and continue to examine, all of it: the past, present, and, to some extent, we must try to guess at the future. We owe it to our patients if to no one else.

Thus the title of this series, *Perspectives In Psychotherapy*. It will, as it implies, attempt to gain continual perspective on our endeavor through the publication of monographs and volumes of thematically related papers. This first volume, Diane Shainberg's *Healing in Psychotherapy: The Process of Holistic Change*, deals very much with the themes that are beginning to emerge in this decade: alienation, fragmentation, the need for relationship, the new requirements for the therapist, the mutuality of the therapeutic encounter. Obviously rooted in immense learning and experience, there is nevertheless a powerful personal thrust and vision in this writing. It is, I believe, an extremely important book, and it is a privilege to have it as the initial volume of the series.

Paul Olsen, Ph.D.

Preface

To heal means to make whole. Both modern science and ancient spiritual teachings remind us that all things in the universe are in flux, are related to one another, and that each thing is itself complete as is. Both science and spiritual teachings indicate that at birth we are whole, a wonder full as is. It is our nature to be whole, full, complete, happy, for otherwise we would not look for it later in life; we would have no sense of its existence if we had never known completeness or if it were not natural to us.

It is the thesis of this book that an individual who is separated by lack of awareness from the essential processes of all forms in nature is psychologically ill. Patients who seek therapy are not aware of their natural wholeness, of the flux and change inside themselves, and of the essential connections to themselves and between all mankind. They are fragmented, fixed, and separated from themselves and others. They compulsively separate themselves from experience by reacting to it and commenting on it. Their judgments, colored by the past, become more real than the experience itself. Psychological illness is the ignorance of who we are in fact and separation from our most natural ways of being which are open and loving.

Healing occurs when we as therapists enable patients to be more fully who they naturally are. Connections are formed with more facets of their inner lives, with the facts of mutability, and with others. They learn to let go of self-consciousness, and to engage in what is taking place without the mental commentary that separates them from the event. They learn to give up compulsivity. The therapist consciousness of the patient reveals what has been covered over by a lifetime of facades is the facilitating environment that enables.

The process of connection with what is begins with the relationship to the therapist. Holistic therapists use not only specific techniques such as interpretations and clarification, but also their presence, which includes their knowledge and experience of consciousness values, attitudes, intuition, and empathic responsiveness. Therapists have knowledge and feeling for certain universal commonalities so that they do not feel separated from their patients. They know from experience that all things in the universe are related. They create and appreciate the moment from a deep awareness that this moment is the essence of life. They know that in this world life is ever changing, loss is inevitable, fullness is our intrinsic nature. They see that human thought in some circumstances is of limited value and are therefore not ruled by it. They can witness thought and feeling coming and going, not being defined by any one fragment knowing all are valid. The holistic therapist has knowledge and experience of thought and feeling sometimes called the Tao or Buddha nature or silence awareness. They are not dependent on their patients for a sense of worth. They are not governed by the need for security from their work. They recognize the process of healing so that they know when the work they have done is sufficient.

All patients come to psychotherapy with their own personal and ego-centric concerns. But each of us wants to find some meaning beyond our small ego and we all want to fit into the larger scheme of things. What we learn is that a man or a woman is one form in nature and expresses certain natural processes common to every form in nature: wholeness, movement, and connection. What the therapist does is help the patient attain a new perspective, so that ignorance of these inner processes is lost. We then find that we are within the fullness we are seeking.

"Each wave thought it was unique and different, until it saw other waves; then it realized there was a whole ocean of waves. One day the wave learned that every wave in the world was made of water. He realized there was an Ocean, but that even though each wave had its own unique form the essential sameness was water."* Once you have achieved the perspective of seeing the essential sameness, you can never lose it. You are no longer separate from others and you share the realization of who you are without all your past evaluations, images, notions. Knowing who you are as is creates an inner condition for change, for being whole in the moment, for connecting with yourself, and allowing others to connect with you.

I have had twenty years of clinical experience as a psychotherapist, teacher, and supervisor. I have been a student of Vedanta and Taoism and have studied Tai Chi. I have been and currently am a student and practitioner of Zen Buddhism. In order to help people reunite with themselves and overcome their separation from the most real and most natural processes inside themselves, I have evolved an integration of Western psychotherapy and Eastern spiritual teachings.

My understanding of psychotherapy and how it is practiced is different from those who have not studied Eastern spiritual teaching and practice.

---

*Personal communication from the Vedanta class of Sandra Eisenstein.

The mind of the healer is distinctly different from the ordinary mind in its attitude and knowledge, although the more realized the person the more ordinary he usually appears, and the more the ordinary world is felt as extraordinary. From knowing myself in both analysis and spiritual practice, it is my experience that it is necessary to empty the mind of preconceptions and notions of how things should go before we can enable others genuinely to change. From my spiritual studies and personal therapy I have faith that each person is intrinsically whole and full and will experience this as I am open to giving them the freedom to exist as they are over time. Knowing from spiritual practice that I am the fullness I seek inside may enable me to be less thrown by patients than I would be without this daily practice of meditation.

Western psychotherapy reveals who we are largely in the realm of thought, feeling, sensation, images, dreams. It focuses on the level of the mind with concepts and feelings. In Eastern spiritual teaching and practice, we learn how to reduce the attachment to thoughts and feelings that create suffering and that separate us from others, and then to experience the silence awareness, the emptiness in which all men are one. We learn what it is to experience without concepts, which is called intuition.

In Eastern spiritual practice we find consistently from experience a level of consciousness in which there is the completeness, and fullness that all people seek. This is the deepest level of the self that is the same for all. Knowing this, we are no longer caught in feeling and thinking that we are separate from others at the deepest level. We are no longer so reactive and dependent on externals for our fullness.

This shift in knowledge, experience and perspective frees us to see the world more as it is and not be so upset by what we see. Psychotherapy enables the person to discover who he uniquely is in fact. Eastern spiritual teaching and practice allows us to know how all people are connected and opens us to the disposition of the "beginner's mind"* necessary to heal others.

My work enables patients to relinquish fragmentation, fixity, and isolation, and to achieve greater awareness of their wholeness, movement, and connection, the processes essential for healing. This book discusses the specific goals and techniques of holistic therapy as I practice it in order to bring about the awareness of wholeness that illuminates what is in our lives.

Diane Shainberg

---

*Shunryu Suzuki, *Zen Mind, Beginner's Mind* (Weatherhill, 1970).

Introduction

In psychotherapy practice we facilitate the ending of separation from living by participating in such a way that the patient forgets the self. The patient is at one with what he is saying, feeling, and therefore ends the separation from the event, and the misery that separation evokes. It is because the patient has remained separate from his experiencing – an object to be changed, a feeling talked about, a life evaluated and commented on – that therapy has at times transient or minimal results. When we end the separation so that the words and feelings are experienced and then let go, we see the central event in healing. For example, the patient begins to feel depressed. He is committed to escaping from it by commenting on it, understanding where it came from, why it is. In healing we shift the focus to what it is, to the experience. We want to be it. At those times when he is being depressed, he is healing. Thus the cure for suffering is the experience of suffering. The commentary on his depression that the patient makes is worse than the experience of depression. When the patient has ended all the commentary telling us that he shouldn't be this way, when will it end, how come we are not helping it, how come this goes on, etc. . . . when all this talk ends, and the patient *is the depression*, then it is a total experience in which there is no observer, no experiencer: there is pure depression. At the moment of such inner experiencing there is a liberation into what is happening. *The person then is what is happening* . . . he is no longer looking for it outside of himself. He is where the action is.

Over and over in therapy we see that when I talk about my depression, "I" am still separate from it. But when *I am being my depression* without commentary, simply being it, there is no "I" anymore; there is only the depression. Thus there is no suffering since there is no "I." When I hang on to the depression by continually commenting on it, then it remains. When a phenomenon is experienced without commentary, it comes to a natural end and something else begins in the mind.

There is no mistaking this healing event when it occurs. In this process of being the event there is always the experience afterwards of knowing that we have found a deeper felt sense of self. I have ended my dread of something by not only being more familiar with it, but also by learning that when I *am it*, it goes away and something else comes up. By thinking about it, commenting on it, it has stayed with me in the form of attachment and craving for release. Being the suffering is ending the suffering.

This does not mean the end of pain, but living in pain at times and then its natural ending with the emergence of something new. Being at one with the inner event is the liberation from it. This realization is the basis of holistic change. The therapist thus works to inspire the patient to participate more whole heartedly in the inner event. His skill is in mindfully guiding the patient over time into the inner event, in keeping with the tempo and needs of the patient. At first the pain may be unbearable so that the therapist guides the patient in keeping with the signs and signals given. The opening or transformation in therapy comes when a person shifts his commitment from escaping tension to becoming rooted in this very moment.

As we heal we know that we are not only in life, but that we also create it as we go . . . we throw ourselves into it and live. At the true moments of healing, the therapist or patient has forgotten the self, there is no awareness of the I . . . there is only absorption or immersion in what is taking place.

The deepest levels of healing are thus unqualifiable, they have no characteristics that are describable, for we are not a separate "I" at those moments to describe them. We are one with what is taking place . . . This is the empathic mode. To break through the separation from the event so that the self is found through forgetting that self is the primary objective and continual practice in healing in psychotherapy.

There are many forms healing takes, from thinking about being more whole to brief flashes of contact with inner experiencing, longer inner experiencing. There is then deep contact with being the experience . . . and letting go of all concepts and finding the silence awareness we all are within which is complete. Here we find the emptiness inside that is our wholeness. This is the healing source within each person. It is the work of the psychotherapist to facilitate patients' discovering this healing source.

I. Facilitating Greater Wholeness: Reducing Fragmentation

The word "whole," according to the *Shorter Oxford English Dictionary,* means 1) in good condition, sound; and 2) in good health, free from disease, healthy.[1] Holistic psychotherapy posits that oneness or wholeness is a state fundamental to the organism, a state we were born into, and which we have covered with self-protective ways of behaving; that we have lost touch with the ways we were at birth: open, giving, and taking to where we were satisfied, complete and happy. Denial of this innate state of wholeness is accompanied by psychological illness. Healing is an aspect of revealing and building on the healthy elements in the organism.

Patients have learned to deny their wholeness, have forgotten their most natural and spontaneous ways of behaving, have been conditioned to think of what is the matter with them, and avoid finding out *what is*, afraid that it will be empty, vile or hopeless. Patients have been accepted by parents when obedient, limited, fixed or conforming with parental images. They have not been given the freedom over time to own what is strong, open and joyful about themselves. They have learned to be afraid to express their own health or soundness for fear that it would separate them further from those on whom they depend.

The patient sees only a small part of any situation, is aware of only a constricted version of all the thoughts imagery, feelings and sensations within himself. Patients often focus on the negative aspect of what is taking place or of who they are. They do not see the constant change in the spectrum of consciousness, but instead hold onto certain thoughts and feelings and define themselves by a small portion of the whole that is available. They make commentary on those thoughts and feelings: "This is good," "This should not be happening," etc. We as therapists see the hopelessness that attachment to only a fragment of our existence brings. When we cannot appreciate the totality of our awareness, we feel trapped by our conditioned thoughts and we are made miserable by the perpetual commentary in our heads. It is the process of accepting without commentary all of our thoughts and feelings as valid, as *who we are as is*, which

1

frees us from the conflict of wanting to be more and different than we are. Once I can see more of who I am, than I *am* more, and I can see that I am not the few conditioned thoughts I have clung to nor the few fragments that were accepted in my growing up. The more aspects of myself I am given the freedom to know and live in without reacting to as right or wrong, good or bad, the more I can witness all the elements of who I am and the healthier I am. One way to activate healing is to learn of both forces, healthy and ill.

The patient is caught in seeing only a small part of the whole. Let us see how hanging onto certain fixed thoughts and feelings with negative reactions is expressed in an initial interview, and see where and how the therapist intervenes to extend the awareness of this constricted and compulsively negative person into an awareness of a larger whole.

A woman called me stating that she had to see me immediately or she would die. Her voice sounded clear. She came on time and sat leaning forward on the couch. She was 27 years old, looked thin, haggard, and unhealthy. Her teeth were a brownish color. She had big, expressive green eyes. Her fingers were long and yellow from smoking. She picked up hunks of her waist-length hair, twisted them around her finger into thin strands, then wound them around her head and neck. She did this incessantly through the session.

She began by saying she thought she was going crazy, felt she could not get enough air in when she breathed, felt she could not go to work any more. She said, "I cannot live from one moment to the next." She said she became so scared when she sat down she had to stand up, although she did not know exactly what scared her. She would stand smoking a pack of cigarettes alone in her apartment in the evening, gazing into space, not thinking of anything, feeling scared. She could not sleep well, although no specific thoughts plagued her. She said she thought "vaguely" about her future. She was nauseated every day, had trouble eating.

She told me that five months ago she had gotten a job with the City government as "an assistant to a high-ranking City official." This job involved considerable responsibility and writing. She felt the people on the job laughed at her behind her back and thought she wasn't smart. Each day at work, she felt that she couldn't do what she had to do. At times she felt confused, not knowing what she was doing there, forgetting what her job was. She then described living alone in an apartment, having come to New York from California, where she had grown up. She did not know why she had come. "It seemed no reason." She "fell" into a City job through a friend's recommendation five years ago and had advanced to her current position. She felt that she would be fired daily, that she wanted to be fired so that she could sleep all the time but didn't know what else to do if she didn't keep her job. She spoke in more detail of her fears on the job. A tinge of pride crept into her voice as she described her responsibilities but the words were completely negative. I asked how she had gotten this job and she described it as "a fluke," being at the right place at the right time, knowing some people who had tipped her off. She insisted it had nothing to do with her capacities. She ended her statements about the job with "I feel this job is going to kill me." Then she went right on talking, not pausing for an instant.

She spoke of living alone. She had a fantasy of having a cozy apartment where she could go home and relax, read, listen to music, have friends visit, eat well. In fact, her apartment was barely furnished after five years; she still had boxes of books around, she had a bed that was too hard, she couldn't eat a regular meal. She could manage a yogurt or a can of tuna fish when alone, but that was about all. She drank a lot of coffee and smoked. She could not read much since she could not concentrate when she was alone. She managed to do work left over from the office, although it often took her far into the night. She spent much time staring out the window or standing up, not knowing what to do with herself. She had trouble falling asleep, fearing she would be sick, wanting to be sick the next day.

At this point came the first pause in her flow of thoughts. I asked, "What is this you call going crazy?", which is where she had started the session.

She described a feeling of holding herself tightly, feeling maybe she should be in a hospital since she couldn't eat or sleep. She said she felt afraid that if she let herself go, she would be a lunatic. She said she would remain in a chair, unable to get up, paralyzed with fear.

I then asked her about any current relationships she might have. She answered that she had a relationship with a married man. She could not understand how she felt towards him, although initially she was flattered that he liked her since he was "a power" in the City government, socially polished, wealthy, handsome, and charming. Her eyes took on more expression as she discussed this man. I asked a few specific questions about him. First I asked, "What could you say of this relationship?" She spoke immediately of loneliness when he left her to return to his wife, the history of their affair seen from her perspective of being repeatedly abandoned by him, her absolute fascination with him. She said with rigid certainty, "It will never change."

I asked more specific questions about this man, such as what fascinated her with him now, how it was to spend time with him, had the relationship changed at all, how did she see herself in terms of wants in this relationship. She began to be involved in talking, she became livelier. She spoke of the man and not of herself, telling me how brilliant he was, how hard he worked, how much power he had, and then she quite suddenly cut herself off from this more open participation in the session and told me with some edge in her voice that it was pointless to talk of him since he had recently told her that he couldn't leave his wife and kids. Then she said arrogantly, "I already knew that. He's not pulling any surprises." She told me that she was "doomed" to stay with this man, living her life waiting for the night of the week she would see him, then feeling lost and left when it was over, only to repeat the same cycle the next week. This had been going on for three years. She said, "This will not change."

I asked her if there were any chink in this belief system, and she said, "You mean that things could be different with us?" I said, "Yes." She said no, she was "aware of the facts of his life." I said he seemed to be getting something from her since he had come around for three years. She seemed to register this as a new idea. She did not respond in words, but I observed that she heard it. She went on to talk of how it was particularly bad that this man could not be more involved with her, since she had no other relationships of meaning. She had "a few friends" but she didn't feel they were real friends, since she couldn't share with them how bad she felt, and if she did, she felt bad. I asked her with whom she had shared this, and she spoke of a woman friend who couldn't accept her behavior, as she was a prude, felt this woman didn't understand her, but then she felt that nobody understood. She saw that this was because she couldn't tell anyone how she spent so much time thinking of different ways to kill herself. She said nastily, "I can't tell anybody I don't know if I want to sit down or stand up, since people aren't usually interested in that kind of stuff." She laughed cynically. Then she said, "I don't have any idea what is going to happen to me. I don't know what I want to do. What is going to happen to me? Do you think you can help me? I'm so scared."

I said I could see that she was scared. I then asked if this was connected with her coming to therapy now. She appeared to be upset by the question; her face became shaky and she said, "This didn't just begin. This has obviously been going on all my life. How can I say when it started?" She added, "there is no one cause for anything," and laughed bitterly.

At this point she said she'd better give me "some background." She became quite fragmented, first talking of her background in college, where she "just happened to end up with a degree in economics, but that doesn't mean I'm an economist. In fact, it doesn't mean anything." She said she "almost killed herself in school"; every time she had to write a paper she would spend hours in the library, be up all night for weeks, feeling she could never do it. She never got to believing she could do the work, even though she made good grades. She spoke of her father's being a professional musician, his violence, his being unhappy and frustrated when he wasn't playing with the symphony orchestra. He wandered around the house yelling at everyone. She was the only one who would fight back. He didn't know how to live his life when he wasn't performing. Often he would hit her, she would hit back, unlike her mother, who was a "ghost." She said her mother had no personality, spent all day fixing her father food, lived in terror of his rages and disappointments, did errands for him. She said contemptuously that she didn't know her sister: "There isn't much to know. She isn't much of a person. We were never close." She then spoke of politics, government, her ideas about the City, how abominably it was run, the mess of it, the ineptitude.

She described her trouble getting food down, how she was losing weight, looked like a skeleton, had bad gums, was afraid to go to the dentist, vomited a few times a week, was so tense she couldn't eat, then got dizzy and vomited. She tried to force food down. Her words began to come faster and faster, scrambling into a knot of fear and hatred discussing people at work.

She then spoke of her last therapist, "a well-respected psychiatrist . . . an incompetent . . . she put me on medication. That didn't help. She didn't understand what I was going through . . . one of those who put you on medicine . . . I think she wanted to do the best she could . . . " She then looked at me with a look of desperation and said, "I don't know if this is the way for me. I can't go on. I wouldn't come unless I felt I just couldn't keep living this way. I don't really believe in therapy, but I don't know what else to do. You've heard me. Do you think you can help me?" I asked, "What would be help?" She smiled and paused, "That is a good question." She registered this, didn't answer, and went on to tell me that she currently smoked three packs of cigarettes a day, her throat was sore, her boss was a moron. Then she said with genuine feeling, "I never worried until recently. I figured I would always do something. I can make jewelry. I did that in California after I finished school. I can write. I can charm people. I always had a boyfriend. So I figured I'd live with a man until . . . " I said, "Until what?" She replied angrily, "You mean marriage?" "You want to tell me I am worried about getting married." I asked, "What are some of your feelings about getting married?" She said, "This isn't it. You don't understand. It isn't any one thing that upsets me. It's everything. It's my whole life that is wrong."

I said that our time was almost up, that I heard her being in a new place now for the first time. She had always thought, as she said, that things would work out, that she could live with a man, do something. Now she wasn't sure, that she was feeling scared by the uncertainty of what was going to be. I said she had talked of two important aspects of her life, her lover and her job, that these were aspects of her daily life that we could go into more deeply. As we talked, we might get clearer about them and discover some new possibilities for her. She then said she thought she could talk to me, adding, "Maybe it can help." She said she liked my waiting room, although it was "a little pretentious with books." She said, "I'm willing to make another appointment." She did not want to go and said so. She sat on the couch breathing deeply, and said, "I don't know if I can make it through another day. Are you going to give me medication?" I said that I was not going to give her medication although I could see she was upset. I said she had expressed some feelings about this from her former therapy, that we could keep it an open issue. She left hesitantly, as though I were forcing her to go. She looked back over her shoulder as she got to the door of the office, sighed deeply, and left, leaving the door open.

In listening to this patient, I ask myself where she is most whole, where in the session the most aspects of who she is come together. I do this in order to enable the patient to connect with her greatest wholeness, where she is most genuine and substantial, since she can do nothing in areas where she is fragmented and compulsive and deeply, habitually negative. I intervene where the patient is most whole as this is the only foundation strong enough on which to build more self-esteem and a firmer relationship. By paying attention to where the patient is most sound or where the most connections come together, the therapist effects more balance in the patient whose vision is off-balance and focused on the negative. Furthermore, exploring any particular fragment lays down new connections and opens new awareness within an habitual mode of perceiving.

In this initial session I intervene with specific questions related to the patient's lover because that area reflects the most holistic aspect the patient presents. This is the place where she actually relates with most emotional involvement in the Present, where she wants something and makes efforts to get it. The patient does not see this wholeness and denies her participation and the movement in the relationship, saying "I know that this can never change." We see that the denial of the movement in this relationship is the illness of the patient. It is the recognition of the actuality of her situation with this man and the possibility of losing him that has brought her to therapy. In this area she now realizes that she cannot have things the way she wants. So this is also her most whole aspect because it is the place of her clearest perception of her reality as well as a recognition of what she wants. She sees that some things in life are out of her control and this upsets her. In this area there is also wholeness as she begins to see some connection in her lifetime pattern of depending on men to take care of her and to make her life secure. This love relationship opens up further

connections with her father, her associations and connections to her
mother and sister and other women in her life.

The effective therapist will intervene where the patient can actually *do*
something right now. He intervenes only where there is already some
wholeness in daily life or some mastery in a situation, otherwise the
patient continues to feel helpless or defeated. The behavior which encom-
passes the most deeply conditioned habitual patterns and the hardest to
change, is often the very area the patient wants to change now.

It is not possible to change anything until we know more of who we are
in fact, how we live in fact. Thus we begin our work where a person is
most wholly aware and can actually put into practice new ways of living.
Some areas in which we intervene are the patient's incipient interests, new
actions of a more constructive nature, emergent processes which are more
open, areas in which anxiety is confronted, and where the patient's des-
criptions or behavior are observably more involved or genuine. Although
this patient cannot get out of her dependent relationship with this man,
this relationship expresses a more genuine interest and involvement than
anything else she mentions. There is something she gets out of and gives to
this relationship. She cannot end her psychosomatic complaints until she
feels stronger inside, so I do not explore them. She cannot get another job
until she feels more competent and inwardly clear about what she wants to
do. However, she can actually be with her lover as she currently is, so that
she can learn some new ways to relate in the moment-to-moment of being
with him.

Now I want to look at some of the specific ways I worked in this
session and the rationale for them. In this session we see the fragmentation
of the patient who thinks only about what will not change, what is wrong
with her life. I introduce the larger whole by focusing on what has already
changed and *what is* in her life without evaluation. The therapist thus
introduces a focus on the larger whole by specific intervention. In this
session, for example:

1. I intervene with questions in the area where the patient is most
whole or where there is least compulsivity. Here that area is a human
relationship.

2. I ask open-ended questions about this man. (I discuss the importance of this type of question further under the section on "inquiry.") In
this first interview, I ask about her boyfriend: "What could you say of
this relationship?", I want to leave the field of response as open as
possible. The questions enable the patient to participate more deeply in
the event of talking to me and give the patient the opportunity to have
an affective experience initiated from inside of herself so that at the very
outset, the patient is encouraged to initiate answers from within and to

emerge with new connections that increase awareness. Involvement in the telling with the therapist reduces the disconnecting, dissociative process for patients.

3. I respond to the needs of the patient for structuring the session. This patient needs to talk a great deal, so that my questions are few and to the point. I meet the needs of the patient without needing the sessions to go any particular way. I maintain a "not knowing" mind open to seeing what the patient needs from me as we go along.

4. I work to clarify the words the patient uses, understanding that the word is not the thing. The thing comprises the many inner events that take place inside the patient and end up in the condensed form we call a word. Since all patients are at times vague and confused, it is important to go into the ambiguous words they use to describe themselves. Unless we get into the meaning behind these words, neither we nor the patient has any idea what the patient is talking about. This patient began by saying, "I am going crazy." By looking into what she meant by "going crazy," the patient found out more of what she thinks.

5. My interpretations articulate where the patient is coming from inwardly and suggests movement. In this session, my interpretation was "You are in a brand new place in your life where you don't know what to do." This implies that there is something other than the fragment "Things won't change," which is how the patient sees her life. I challenge this fragment by referring to something new, opening up the field of awareness to where the patient hears that she was already changing and that the actuality was that she didn't know what to do as yet, which is neither bad nor good. By not reacting, I conveyed the lack of judgment of this inner condition with my objective attitude. I tacitly implied that there is a value in looking at *what is*, not fixing or making things better. To be more whole we have to begin to see who we are in fact. We move from thinking about what is happening to experiencing it. As one becomes more whole, one begins to question, and questioning is painful because it entails wakefulness to uncertainty.

6. My interpretations clarify the actuality of what I empathically hear the patient is now living in, going through. As we therapists listen, we ask, "How can I express to the patient in an ordered way the actuality of what he is going through?" It might be as simple as telling them that we hear how worn out they are, how they are taking a lot of burden on themselves, how they are not clear right now about what they want, etc. Clarifying the actuality in an interpretation enables the patient to make some order out of what often feels like the disorder of his life, and confronts him with some element of what he might be struggling with at this particular juncture.

7. I observe the actual behavioral changes in the patient in the session. With this patient I see that she is avoiding something with non-stop talk, that she appeals to me, then degrades me. I also observe how she relaxes near the end of the session so that for a few moments she can let in what I say. She hears me say that this man must be getting something from being with her. She comes into the session extremely tense and leaves a bit more relaxed. I observe that she can make use of the therapy and that although she might block awareness of some of her changes, she has let go of her fixed position and lets in some new information, so that I am hopeful about our work. Observing this change in response to hearing me, I cannot take seriously her denial of any change. I will not be swayed by her compulsive fragmentation into negativism. I do not underestimate the value of the healing power of the organism in relationship. I am aware of what a meaningful difference it makes to have someone you can talk to, who you think understands something of what you are going through. I see that taking place so that my attitude at the end of the session is that a lot has changed and that we could both let go of having to pretend to know what will happen between us.

8. I focus my comments on her getting and giving in this relationship and thus work again on extending the fragment towards greater wholeness by saying that her boyfriend is getting something by staying with her. The implication here is that she can and has given and thus has gotten. This is a more whole perspective than "nothing can ever change."

9. I watch in the session for the moment of greatest participation on the part of the patient. Although much of what she says has the character of a litany repeated thousands of times in her head, the talk about her boyfriend is more genuine, more affectively participated in by the patient. By inquiring at the *growth edge*, we direct the patient's attention to an inherent wholeness that already exists within of which she is ignorant. We extend awareness beyond the familiar clinging to habitual feelings or thoughts to a new and more whole way to perceive.

Before going further, let us look at the process of fragmentation and see more of what it is.

1.1 What is fragmentation?

Patients are afraid of being open and letting be and finding out more of who they are. Instead, patients cling to a *very few thoughts and think about them all the time,* making endless commentary on them. They define themselves on the basis of these constricted thoughts, feelings, images, fantasies, sensations, dreams. Their view of themselves and the world is narrow, repetitive, self-preoccupied, and spurns anything that refutes their conditioned way of seeing themselves and others.

Fragmentation is one form of illness. In this process the person shows us that he does not know the whole of himself. He only knows the aspects of himself which he has been taught were acceptable as a child and which he has used to define the whole of himself. He may say "I can't do it," "I want to make friends but I don't know how," "I have to get rid of this problem of my mother, wife, boss, money, sex, etc." The person in fragmentation does not let go of the fragment and experience the larger whole of his existence, does not see his commonalities with his fellow man. In fragmentation the patient does not know how to find out new things about himself and life that stretch beyond his past because he is attached to fixed notions of self and others. He does not inquire, go into, or even think over what he is saying. He remains fixed in the fragment and believes that it is all there is. It represents a static, deeply entrenched belief system. In this way he does not experience *how things are changing* in life. For him, life remains fixed — "I cannot get what I want." He focuses on this. He does not want to look at it. He demands that "it" change without even knowing clearly or experientially what the problem is. The patient does not see and own how there are things he does get. He won't go into the pain of it, *be* "not getting what I want," feel it deeply with all of his being. He separates himself from knowing it by always thinking *about* it and fighting it or escaping from ultimately experiencing it. He cannot see it as only one thought among many others and see that what makes him so miserable is his own endless commentary on the fact of not getting what he wants. In fragmentation the person does not appreciate that the part emerges from a whole in which there are many possibilities, for he has lost touch with the whole out of which the jagged part is torn.

The more the person focuses on bits of himself, the more he feels separated from himself and his fellow man. He does not see himself as part of a larger whole. He is not able simply to let his thoughts flow and see them all as valid, ever changing.

In illness a person does not experience what is going on outside his own head, he cannot assimilate feedback without distorting it. There is then difficulty with letting in experience or letting go of past ideas, since letting go may lead to anxiety or not knowing. The person manufactures the world out of his own head based on his parents' notions of how life is supposed to be and on his self-image. When something new appears that does not conform to his pre-established schema, he avoids the anxiety of discordance by stopping his feelings. He learned this habit of not perceiving or feeling in new ways by being too frightened to do this with his mother, father, or significant others. They indicated "stop" when he did or said certain things. They did not give him the freedom to discover for himself who he is, how things are for him, what he wants to do and be.

The culmination of having to see things in a rigid, stopped way is diminished experiencing, dim feelings and a paucity of emotional experiences. We often see people who feel themselves to be incompetent, inept, when in fact they hold good jobs, have accomplished certain things in life. But they do not experience owning what they have done. They have learned to cut off the experiencing process because it may conflict with images of how they are supposed to see themselves or the world that offer them the only security they have ever known.

The only way to break this cycle of endlessly stopping whatever provokes anxiety is to be given freedom. The therapist's attitude of openness to knowing the patient *as is* grants freedom to be who he is and to be aware of whatever comes up and let it be without judgment. In this safe ambience, the patient can learn to increase awareness and heal fragmentation.

The healthier the person the more he sees the incredible power of thought in his life. He thinks, "I don't have any close friends. I have no one to be with today," and he feels bad. He thinks, "Tomorrow I will go to the party and meet some new people," and he feels good. He thinks, "I don't have enough money to buy that house," and he is sad. He thinks, "When I get home I will eat a delicious meal," and he feels good. He is deeply affected and often tyrannized by what he thinks. It is our thoughts, our commentary on the actualities of life, that create recurrent suffering. We comment, "If it weren't for my mother I would respect myself now and could do more of what I want. If only I did not have these parents . . . Why do I have this fat body . . . " etc. The actuality may be painful, but the thoughts sustain the pain. We thus see the limited value of certain kinds of thoughts and recognize that these endless commentaries sustain our misery and limit our possibilities.

The work of the therapist is to clarify the notions people have of who they are, and then to challenge them, to point out the notions that block growth, and to enlarge these notions by expanding the patients' awareness of the larger whole of thought, feeling, imagery, fantasy, sensation, dream life. Initially we do this by providing a nonthreatening presence so that patients can drop their facades by having the freedom to discover more of the whole of all the aspects of who they are.

A healthy person knows he can be many ways, that he changes how he sees himself, that he has been different ways and each of them has equal weight. If he thinks or feels "I am sad," he knows the thought or feeling will go and another will come. He doesn't define himself with the thought. When he doesn't escape but experiences the sadness, he finds that it disappears and something else emerges in his mind. If he fights or escapes it, it remains as something to be feared. The healing process turns concept into experience.

Once we allow ourselves to experience something, it goes away. It is avoidance that creates conflict. Fragmentation is avoidance of the full spectrum of consciousness. It is a manifestation of clinging to the past and dreading the future. It reveals a difficulty being open to what comes up in the present.

To be free from anything, I have to know what that thing is. As I open to knowing and letting it exist and do not clutch at it, it fades off into air. By accepting the feeling and not fighting it, we learn that it exists and then it is gone. By living in what we feel and think, we come to know the ever-changing nature of life. We do not dread a feeling so much once we open to it, let it happen, for it is familiar and therefore not so fearsome. The healthy person can sit and say, "I'm sad because I can't get this and that, and I dwell on it and elaborate it, then I am more depressed and I drink to avoid it, etc. Then next time it comes, I am again afraid to be it. But as I let it in and am sad, there is no thinking at all. There's just sadness. Then it goes away and something else happens." These times of experiencing without concepts are the greatest times of healing in therapy and they bring an end to fragmentation. In the moment of experiencing there is no sense of "I," there is a loss of separation from the event. The person *is* the event and is whole. It is our separation from the wholehearted participation in being what we are that creates fragmentation. As I can be my experiencing, I also see my consciousness changing so that new aspects of who I am emerge into awareness continually.

In states of health we see that thoughts come and go, move, flow, all thoughts are equal, there is no good or bad, no more or less important. In fragmentation, a person lives in a circular, narrow version of rigid, conditioned notions. A few common fragments we hear are:

I can't do it.
I have to be helped, taken care of.
I am no good.
Why can't I be like X?
Why can't I do X?
I want it to be the same as before.
It's got to be better. What should I do?
I'll get even when . . .
I'll never get better.
Never again will I trust anyone, show my feelings.

I should have been able to . . .
You should . . .
I have to do this (e.g., get married, loss weight, leave home, get interested in some-
    thing) but I can't.

Underlying these are more rigidly held forms of thought/feeling fragments represented in ways of seeing life and one's place in it. These
notions leave a person convinced that there is a way their life should go.
Fragments are notions of life rather than an interest and openness in seeing
how life is. Here are some deeply held common fragments which ignore
the whole of who one is, fix on certain ideas, and attach feeling to the
ideas as if they were one's true nature rather than just passing thoughts:

I deserve to be loved.
I will get what I want if I work hard for it.
I must get what I need.
Life will get better.
I will not survive alone.
I should not suffer terrible pain.
I must not show my vulnerability.
I must know.
I cannot stand not to be sure.
I can't live life without some form of approval.
I can't love without a mother or father figure to love me, tell me what to do.
I cannot be master of my life, able to stand on my own if necessary, not dependent
    on what others think of me.
I am afraid of other people, unable to live in this fear, unable to trust others.

By holding onto these fragments, the patient encourages the therapist
to focus on pathology with him. This is how he was treated when growing
up. A person with little sense that he can affect his own life must first
begin to feel that he can in fact initiate from within. However, the patient
demands the therapist's "help," not knowing that *you can't change anything until you first are clearer as to what is going on inside yourself*,
letting yourself be *as is* without avoidance. This knowing ourselves in our
various elements, in our changes, knowing that we exist in depth in various
inner states, is what gives us the inner strength to make changes.

A whole person moves into uncertainty convinced that he is always
changing, open to what is new. A fragmented person lives mechanically on
the basis of what he has been taught by others, not what he has found for
himself. The therapist encourages the patient to find for himself by discovering his own inner position. In order to do this, the patient must be
with himself, get to know himself. The work of the therapist is to help a
person get interested in himself *as is*.

1.2 Clarifying the problem and the patient's way of living in it

The patient wants to solve certain problems when he first enters treatment. He tells you the problems he wants to solve but he does not experience clearly what the problem *is* — it takes time to find out what a problem is. The patient does not know the complexities of the problem since he has not reflected on it or lived in it wholeheartedly, without avoidance in one form or another. Although it sometimes sounds as if the patient knows what he wants, inquiry often reveals that the person does not know how come he craves something so deeply, how come he does things the way he does, why certain ways are experienced as inevitable, or what he really wants in life other than pleasure or security that lasts a brief span. *We thus often see a person who is ignorant of who he is and what he wants.* He takes the masks and pretenses to be his true nature. Since he has lost touch with who he is, the person feels that he doesn't create his own life out of his actions and his mind. Instead he nurtures the illusion that he can control the results in life. He does not know the relationship between responsibility for actions and getting what he wants in living. The therapist knows from experience that when people are in a non-judgmental environment where they are given the freedom to be who they are *as is,* they will drop their facades and so end their ignorance of the greater wholeness that they truly are outside the domain of compulsive thought and feeling.

Being egocentric and feeling separate from his fellow man, the patient does not deeply feel that help exists for him, that there is support for him in the universe, that anybody would want to help him. This separation between man and man is the result of not being able to get beyond the individual fragment to the larger whole to a level of awareness which is the same for all men, connecting all men.

A woman came in saying that she wanted either a friend or a lover but that she couldn't get both in the same person. Her lover has premature ejaculation and so had two earlier lovers. Her lovers had all left her. She says, "I want to find someone who can satisfy me." The rest of the session was spent talking of her anger at her boyfriend whom she is thinking of marrying.

This woman has no sense yet of what her problem is although she talks about one fragment of it: Men leave her in one way or another, and she doesn't like this. So far she does not see her own actions in creating any of this situation. She sees only a fragment: "I want a boyfriend." She wants the therapist to do something, but before anything she has to know what it is for her to be with men, what she is withholding from herself, what the payoff is in their leaving, the price of her fear, etc.

This woman says, "I want to find someone." She has found many men but they leave her. She does not puzzle over this but throws it out as if unrelated to her behavior. In the intitial interview she says, "I'm not getting what I want, what I need. I'm not getting the love I need." She focuses on the sexual problems of her lover. She does not mention her own sexual behavior nor does she appear interested in it.

She mentions briefly her father, who left the family when she was 8, her mother's always having lovers, her grandmother's hatred of her mother's sexual behavior, her own high intellect. She mentions her wish to be a doctor and her loneliness as a child, her drive to achieve. She does not see how this affects her relations with others.

She mentions how she got what she wanted by hurting others. She does not see this connection in her current life and how she lives it out. She is not aware of how furious she is and how this affects others around her. She has an image that a woman is supposed to be a femme fatale, love them and leave them as her mother did, but she cannot see herself as driven to have lovers. She does not mention intimacy with another, nor does she seem sensitive to the feelings of others, nor does she know this about herself.

Her experience is that she deserves to be loved. She is not aware of how this is inwardly difficult for her. She is not aware of how little she cares for others. Thus through inquiring, this "problem" of wanting a man and what *it is* must slowly, more clearly, come into focus. The patient asks, "Should I marry this man who has premature ejaculation?" "What should I do now?" "How do I know I can do any better?" As she searches for external answers, the therapist will move to open up the experiences she brings in with questions that move her more into herself. The patient says, "I am not getting what I want. I want out of this." However, as we listen, we hear that the patient is so busy, so distracted, that she doesn't know what "this" is. We ask what this is. She might say, "This is my unhappiness," yet she does not yet know that her unhappiness is her own thoughts which say over and over, "I deserve love," without seeing that saying so will not bring love, that she, like other humans, is responsible for her own actions. We inquire into the source of her inner unhappiness and the source of her happiness, her experience, thus moving the "problem" into a *process of clarifying the actuality she lives in.*

In this situation it is helpful to begin with the patient's experiences with her lover. The questions open this out so that in each session new connections are laid down in the form of new associations, thoughts and feelings, images, sensations, fantasies, dreams, so that the patient brings more to the process of discovering that it is her own thoughts, her own ways, her feelings which are the source of her suffering. It is her craving to escape the problem which is the problem. In looking at it, going into it, discovering who she is, there is no problem. There is a person demanding to be loved and *thinking* there is a problem.

This patient is living her impatience and degradation with me in the session. I confront this way of living and I confront her behavior with me as denying herself certain possibilities in the situation as well as denying the possibility that I had anything of value to say. We continue to look at how she *lives* in the session with me as we work. We look at how this might relate to her lover. Later we shall look at her loving others. It is the mind of the patient that is the problem. But when she entered therapy she experienced the problem as external to her.

As we work to clarify the actuality, whatever it is, we see new elements of how the patient *is* it and participates *in* it. Thus by clarifying actuality and how the patient lives it in daily life, lives it in the session, the patient is being more whole. The patient comes to see *she is it*, she is not separate from her problem . . . her ways of thinking, feeling and acting are the problem. In disovering her own actuality, the patient comes to feel she creates her own life from inside and begins to feel more whole.

1.3 Inquiry and Exploration

How do we enable a person to be more whole, to reach an inner condition of being able to make choices? One of the key ways of working in psychotherapy is inquiry. The therapist creates questions that inspire further looking. Asking questions appears very simple until we discover in supervision that many therapists do not know how to ask questions that engage the patient, arouse interest in the patient, or surprise him into thinking and looking further into things. Many therapists ask stock question — "What did you feel about that?" or "What was that like for you?" — rather than questions that move the patient into the event so that it is experienced in the session. Participation in answering questions and telling is when the patient is most whole. Thus originality and imagination in forming questions is essential to facilitating wholeness.

The first issue is *where* to intervene with questions. The second issue is *how to inquire*, what sorts of questions move the process further and deeper so that fragmented thinking opens up into greater wholeness. Too often, therapists avoid exploring certain issues that could benefit the patient for fear of being shoved around or trapped by the patient.

A supervisee came in telling me that she was almost falling asleep in sessions with a certain patient. She could not understand this. She spoke about the process in the work, the dynamics, what she saw of the interaction, and here she mentioned that the patient smiled at the beginning of the session in a very sweet way that she felt masked considerable hostility. The obvious question to ask this patient was what this smile was saying. The therapist became edgy and admitted feeling scared of the patient but not knowing why. She feared that the patient was disappointed with the work and might leave. She realized that she never questioned the way the patient was behaving in the session. She then spoke of her own need to respond with a smile and how false the whole thing felt. She felt that she was failing, not doing enough, not knowing what to do with this patient, and therefore did not inquire more deeply into observable phenomena.

This example indicates what happens in therapy when the therapist colludes with the patient to protect his own worth or security in work with patients by not questioning what is taking place between them in session. Specific, particular inquiry into events is often blocked by the therapist who is dependent on the patient for something, or is upset by the patient's potential anger or devaluation of his work.

One of the most common occurrences in therapy is the formation of an alliance in which the deal is "I won't upset you too much if you don't upset me." Here we see a shallow level of work or a tense, stuck feeling reported by the therapist. Much of this passivity serves to protect the therapist from the patient's anger and disappointment. The end result is that important questions are not asked.

1.4 Observation

How do we know what questions to ask a person? This has to do with closely hearing what he says and enfolding this, but also with observing the way he relates to us, his way of being in the world, his relating in the work we do. For example, we see that the patient is increasingly relaxed, involved in talking. The patient tells us he gets nothing out of the work. We *see* this is not true. We do not react to the patient's words when we can see what is actually taking place. We see a whole larger than the words.

By carefully observing the patient, we see when there is a need for more questioning and active participation, when there is a need for silence, when humor can be effective in opening up the relating, when a more serious way of working is indicated.

The basic idea is that when the therapist is giving highest value to seeing how the patient is rather than how he would like him to be, careful observation is possible. An open mind and concentrated observation lead to clear perception and correct actions in therapy. They lead to knowing what sorts of questions to ask. As the therapist sharpens his concentration in observation and gives high value to seeing things as they are, he begins to feel that the patient is as he is, and thus is complete no matter what that way is. The therapist sees that the patient can be no other way. There is less longing for anything to go differently. By observing, we are seeing the whole person as he lives in the microcosm of the session. We *see* the hurt, sorrow, anger, humor, tenderness, awkwardness, and feel where the patient is coming from inside. We are not fixed on the content of the communication. We are *at one with what the patient is living*; there is no separation between what we are hearing and our participation in feeling it as we go along.

We *see clearly* that a patient is nasty. The tone, manner, way of looking, are degrading. The words may or may not be nasty. In seeing this, we see who the person is right now. We do not long for this person to be kind and considerate, as we *see this is impossible. Only by seeing what is can we let be what is and give the patient the freedom to get to know who he is in fact.* When we can see that the patient is terrified to be in relationship from moment to moment and will not drop his self-protective guard, we do not expect him to be at ease; we understand when he complains that he can't talk to us except in a frightened way. That is what we see: that he is afraid. We see the patient's attempts to control himself and then us, and we know it cannot be otherwise. We are then able to move with how the patient is and stop wishing it were different. We can point out this fear to the patient or not, but first we have to see the fear in order to respect the patient's attempts to control it beyond anything else. In this way there is relaxation in simply seeing what is there — as a fact — seeing it as another form in the universe that suffering takes, not as something to be changed. When the therapist can see what is, let be what is, the patient is given the space to discover who he is in a safe, facilitating environment. In this field of interaction, trust can begin and grow.

Most of the patients we see are terrified simply to be with another person, just to be in the openness of pure relating. They need to have problems or something to talk about, something to distract them from the phenomenon of just being together with another. Without these problems, they are *with you,* aware of you, aware of themselves. Patients work to have problems, for without them, they are in touch with their being, which at times is unbearable pain and fear. So the patient says with panic or concern, "I have nothing to talk about this week." This often expresses the deep anxiety of simply being together with another, the terror of open relating, the terror of remaining open.

1.5 Observation that helps form questions

Let us look at an example of how attentive observation leads to asking questions that open the process:

A colleague referred a patient to me after working with him for one year. My colleague explained, "I can't take it anymore. He's the most boring, negative patient. We aren't able to talk." The patient had had five previous therapists. He had seen therapists on and off since the age of 18 when he had beaten up several college friends, broken a window, and not known why. At 26, he entered full-time therapy with a highly negative attitude. He was sullen, nasty, quite perceptive about how therapy was "supposed to work" and hadn't with him. He seemed to delight in the number of people he had "defeated" on the surface, but also appeared frightened and furious.

He was currently 26, a recording studio engineer, spent most of his time sleeping or building electronic equipment while not working, and could not remember anything before the age of 12 when his father had had a heart attack. An only child, he now lived alone with his mother and had no friends. His thoughts were consumed with how to murder or get revenge on a group of men who had stolen a record idea from him which made a lot of money, none of which he got.

Bitter, cynical, this man complained from the first of what I was not doing for him. Talk of hopelessness about therapy occurred in most sessions.

This was the ninth session. I had observed the patient's black humor, his slight smile when talking. I observed his energy level go up slightly as he described his interest in music, in electronic equipment.

Pt: (Comes in 10 minutes late. Frowning, sits down like a robot.)

Th: (Pausing to see where patient goes. As usual, he is silent, scowling.) You're late. You've been late the last few times.

Pt: (no response apparent)

Th: What do you imagine I feel when you're late?

Pt: It doesn't matter to me.

Th: (beginning to sing softly) "It doesn't matter to me." (puts a melody to this) I bet you've sold a million copies of that tune. (sings softly again) "It doesn't matter to me."

Pt: (smiling the least bit) I have no thoughts about being late. I told you I can't think.

Th: How do you know you have no thoughts if you never had any? (pause. The patient is now yawning, blinking his eyes, which is his usual behavior) What do you feel coming here?

Pt: It's a kind of waste.

Th: I'm deeply flattered. You always said "It's a waste." Now it's only kind of a waste. Things are getting better.

Pt: (laughing for the first time) I meant to say it is a waste. My mother pays for it, thank God. (pause) I never had any relationship with any therapist. The last one couldn't take it. I can't see any point to what we're doing.

Th: Maybe you aren't even here. I mean you have no thoughts, we have no relationship, nothing happens here. Maybe it's a fantasy that you're actually sitting here.

Pt: You sound like somebody in the record business, nuts. (slight smile) I was thinking of going to the movies today instead of this. At least you pay your money and you get something.

Th: But there is one fascinating thing. You came late. But you left yourself 35 minutes to be here. I can't figure that one out.

Pt: I can't figure that out either. (beginning to appear more alert)

Th: Especially since we have no relationship at all. You insist adamantly on that.

Pt: (looks directly at me, laughing slightly) You don't believe me, do you.

Th: I am impressed with your activity. Your robust insistence that nothing is happening here.

Pt: (opens up briefcase) I cut a record with a Haitian band. Nobody speaks English. We did this whole session with nobody understanding a word of what anybody said. (smiles) But the rhythm is terrific. The words don't matter that much.

During the rest of the session he was more involved in talking about getting this group together, saying it was hopeless but adding how good they were. Maybe he could cut the record. He moved away from his negative and compulsive position that "he couldn't do it" after I observed that a slightly wacky humor would engage him. For the next two sessions he was a bit more lively and he asked me if I wanted to listen to the tapes he had made at work with the same band. I replied that I did.

For the next several months he brought in equipment and discussed it. I asked many questions. I was interested in what he had to say. He spoke not at all about himself for months.

By observing his humor, his interest, I moved with where he could talk and with *how* he could participate – with humor. My inquiry was active as this was what I sensed he needed. The nature of the inquiry came out of my clear observation of the patient. I acted on what I saw he needed to be able to reveal himself further and move into greater wholeness from within.

1.6 Interpretation of struggle as a means to greater wholeness

The patient may not see that he is struggling to be free of the confines of his past. He does not see that struggle is related to intelligence and having some kind of wakefulness taking place. As long as people are struggling to be who they are, to find who they are authentically, to live more wholly in the Present, to be more connected to themselves and others, to live using more of themselves, there is great hope. It is thus working in the direction of holism to interpret to patients what we see them struggling with at different times during the progress of therapy. Inherent in the notion of struggle is movement, which indicates that the patient is moving in new directions, different from those with which he began the treatment, or different from what he is aware of in his present life. In life we all go through certain common struggles. These struggles are acknowledged in all of the great spiritual writings: the Bible, the Vedanta, the I Ching, the Buddhist sutras. When we tell patients what they might be struggling with at the present point in treatment, they often feel a surge of energy as they begin to sense that they are active in the process of creating their own life. Here are some basic human struggles *around which interpretations can be made* towards the end of facilitating greater wholeness in the patient. Articulating these struggles of the patient can often organize a great deal of content which would otherwise remain disorganized for the patient.

Some Common Human Struggles

Listed below are some central issues that people struggle with in the process of psychotherapy. These struggles form the source for many of our interpretations to patients of what they are engaging in the healing process.

To increase our awareness of who we are intellectually, emotionally, imaginatively, and sensorily so that we are more inside. The more we know of who we are the more we are.
To want to understand conceptually what is taking place or what has taken place. (and not what others have told you.)
To know from our own experience what is taking place now and in the past. (and not what others have told you.)
To find out our own personal truth. To discover what we want.
To realize one will die.
To live in physical health.
To be able to be ourselves and not who others think we should be.
To see and know the concepts and notions we have of who we should be which were handed to us by significant others.
To see and know the concepts and notions we have of how other people are.
To see the concepts and notions we have of how other people should treat us.
To see the concepts and notions we have of how our life should go.

To see that certain concepts and notions make us miserable and are of limited value. Then to discover the importance of letting them go.

To experience some notions and concepts as a script written by our parents and not by us.

To begin to write our own script based on what we experience and what we want, thus breaking habitual ways of living.

To see things more as they are not as our concepts would have them, and to deal with things as they are.

To take things in that happen to us.

To be active, to initiate.

To be passive when appropriate.

To work productively and creatively.

To be independent.

To be dependent.

To live with pleasure and to feel deserving and grateful for it.

To live with psychological pain and to see it as inevitable at times.

To understand the function and growth promoting nature of genuine pain as distinct from the clinging to pain in the form of commentary on it. This is the difference between experiencing it and talking about it.

To see how we create our own pain.

To be able to live with and without others, and not to feel we will fall apart when alone.

To be more self-sufficient.

To discover what we truly want so that we can stop closing off our possibilities and to set priorities.

To discover our assets and our limits.

To move in the direction of getting what we want.

To experience how other people can help us and how we can help ourselves.

To see our basic patterns in living and to see those which open and those which close our possibilities in living.

To gain clarity as to how our past relationships and behaviors still play a part in the present.

To experientially re-live our past traumas so that we can come to a greater understanding of our current suffering.

To experientially re-live our past traumas and events so that we can feel a greater empathy for ourself.

To be in an environment where we can express the totality of our feelings so that we can be more authentic.

Letting go of our past conditioned ideas of how life should go and dealing with it as it happens.

Dealing with ourself, other people, and life as they are, not as we wish they were.

Realizing we are totally responsible for our actions but we do not have control over the results of these actions.

To see how we avoid relating.

To understand the reasons for our avoiding relating.

To be in relating and to see that being human is to be in relationship.

To express our loving feelings to others and with ourself.

To express our sexuality.

To let ourself BE in relationship, and not to have to be certain ways.

To find moments of fullness and completion in living.

To reduce the distractions of the mind so one lives fully in the Present Moment.

To learn that thoughts and feelings come and go, and to discover how all are valid, they are simply THERE coming and going when the mind is open and not compulsively identified with some fragment.

To live more wholeheartedly in THIS VERY MOMENT.

To clarify conflicts and their source.

To reduce comparison with others and to appreciate our uniqueness.

To know and feel in what ways we are similar to all our fellow beings and to free our humanness and connection with others.

To examine our relationship to suffering.

To discover that when we can experience our suffering it comes to a natural end and something new can begin. By avoiding suffering it doesn't end.

To examine our purpose in being alive.

To create our own life as we go along based on our inner voice.

To mourn our losses and be grateful for our gains.

To see life is constantly changing and to let go of trying to make things last, and cling and fix.

To be more aware of our senses. To see, hear, taste, touch and smell and to BE present in
them is to feel life as full and rich.
To develop a friendlier feeling to ourselves and others.
To experience the opening of our heart and see and know the love within ourselves. We then
know we have to express it by finding the right people or situations that release it.
To see how we live in relationship in the therapy relationship.
To try out new ways of relating in the therapy relationship.
To see how we can soothe ourself and others.
To explore how our self-esteem is regulated and how we maintain it, lose it, regain it.
To discover our fears, the causes of our fears, to clarify how we can overcome fears.
To see how the insights gained in therapy can be put into practice in daily life.
Seeing how unhappy we have truly been, and experiencing what brought us to therapy.
To feel our potential for living through experiencing how we have moved in therapy.
To learn how to validate ourself.
To reduce self-preoccupation and to be more interested in others and in the world.
To realize that change is an ongoing process from the beginning to the end of life.

These are some of the struggles all patients engage as they move
towards greater inner wholeness, and it is these and other struggles around
which the therapist makes interpretations.

1.6.1 Examples of interpretation of the patient's current struggles

A patient talks about how she doesn't know what she wants to do with her life, she
doesn't see any direction, she leaves things quickly. She feels agitated and frightened
much of the time. I hear that she is struggling with experiencing more of herself; she
sees herself more clearly. I say, "You are now able to experience more of yourself.
You are letting in more experiencing although this isn't easy. You see more of your
confusion. You didn't know much of who you were last year." The patient states she
is feeling worse than when she started therapy. I say, "You are feeling worse as you
are feeling more. You used to block out and numb your feelings; this is a struggle as
it means feeling better and worse. But certainly feeling more. You are a more feeling
person." The focus of the interpretation is on what the patient struggles with now in
life.
    A patient speaks of feeling terribly anxious. She has told her mother that she will
not go shopping with her, that she will choose her own dress for a family affair. The
patient feels that she still needs her mother and that she only pretends not to as she is
angry about being a baby. I suggest that she is moving to be more independent and
this is new for her, that her struggles will create many repercussions, but that once
she embarks on the struggle, she will find she cannot go back on it or forget it.
    A patient is thinking about her mother's death from cancer a year ago. She talks
of not knowing what went wrong when her mother got worse, blaming herself for
not changing doctors, feeling that her mother would have lived if they had tried
another program, etc. I mention to her that she didn't ever understand what went
wrong in the treatment, that the doctors had not expected her mother to die so
quickly, no one had given her any clear explanation of what had taken place. Of
course she would be feeling a deep need to understand why her mother had died in a
literal way. The patient then talks of a wish to go to the doctor and her fear that he
would think she was nuts since this was a year later. I say that this is her tendency, to
think that life is supposed to be lived in a certain way which rules out her wishes. She
has so many notions of how things are supposed to be done that she doesn't dare to
act on what comes authentically from herself. After delaying for a year, the patient

begins the process of trying to learn more about the cause of her mother's death, thus relieving herself of the burden of blame.

A woman complains bitterly about her depression, which is related to seeing her parents more clearly. She has denied this for many years, always idealizing her parents and saying that nothing much went wrong in growing up. As she looks into what happened, she becomes upset and angry and then quite sad. She feels therapy has gypped her of a happy childhood. I say that she is getting to know more of the actuality of her life, who she is in fact – not some unreal person. She is letting go of some of her pretenses, and in giving up she will be getting more, will be more real. I say that letting in more of her depression says to me that she is stronger now and can struggle and live with where she is in fact. I say that formerly she maintained the pretense that all was fine and was continually strained by living with this fiction. I say, "Avoiding your depression almost made you crazy." She agrees that her life had been felt as a terrible strain and that there was a chance that finding out more was going to be at least different from keeping up the pretense. The patient appears more relaxed after this session, and begins to cry openly with me for the first time.

1.7 Recognizing wholeness and facilitating differentiation

When we recognize the person's being more whole in the session, we appreciate this and at those moments, we give the patient the freedom to grow up, to be different from us, to be more who they are as distinct and as similar to us. The very recognition of those moments of change and greater wholeness in the session is what facilitates differentiation. The very recognition of those moments in the session in which there is an increase in awareness, where the patient is letting in and being more of himself in extensity and intensity, gives us a new image of the patient. By seeing the patient as more whole, we are saying that it is okay to be this, we recognize and appreciate this change, we welcome it. Our attitude is different from that of the mother and father who were threatened by the increased autonomy of the child.

All his life the patient experiences going with what someone else wants. He believes that what he says is magically and automatically believed by the other person because they are essentially the same. He is accustomed to systems of interaction that produce predictable and therefore safe results.

In every instance where wholeness is facilitated, differentiation is also enhanced. When we ask for the patient's responses, we are enabling him to discover his own distinct responses. A question such as "I don't understand. Can you say more on this . . . ?" calls on him to recognize the other person as separate from him. By remaining outside the patient's system of control, the therapist moves the patient to be increasingly on his own. He is thus thrust into uncertainty and anxiety . . . etc., which are growth-inducing in an environment where a person (therapist) is not threatening. In this way we do not act or do what the patient expects, and in this way we are enabling the patient to contain more anxiety and thus to be more whole if he stays in interaction with us. Remaining steady when the patient lives out some of the more difficult feelings with us such as hostility, fear, hopelessness, confusion, enables the patient to bear with more of his own feelings and thereby to be more differentiated from us.

All forms in therapy of letting the patient work more on his own, to express things in his way and to be left in the session to struggle to find his own ideas, enable the patient to find out that he is indeed more whole and thereby more differentiated. This also occurs as we ask questions, going into specifics so that people move from global undifferentiated ambiguous responses to more differentiated discriminatory responses.

As we work to focus on what is happening right now, we inevitably put patients in touch with their distinctiveness and their separateness. Throughout the therapy we give the patient the freedom to teach us what he needs through attending closely to his signals concerning anxiety tolerance, response to question, silence, integrating or not hearing interpretations of a certain kind, structure, mood, level of discourse. Such attention is the basis of empathy. As the therapist takes his signals from the patient, the patient is heard and is thus granted the freedom to be more on his own, and in this way, too, differentiation and greater wholeness are encouraged.

All things are related in therapy. As the therapist is more comfortable with himself, freer inside himself from reacting, needing less from others for his own fullness, not dependent on a particular set-up, being interested to see people as they are, so the patient is more comfortable in therapy, freer to discover himself without having to worry about meeting the needs of the therapist or reacting to the tensions of the therapist. As the patient discovers new aspects of how and what he thinks and feels and senses and imagines and dreams, he is more. This greater wholeness begins with a therapist who gives value to seeing things as they are and to ending the reactive mind that is dependent on others to fulfill its likes and dislikes.

References

1. *The Shorter Oxford English Dictionary*, prepared by William Little, H. W. Fowler, and J. Coulson (Oxford: Oxford University Press, 1956), pp. 2422–23.
2. Dogen Kigen, *Mystical Realist*, trans. Hee-Jin Kim (Tucson: University of Arizona Press, 1980).

II. Facilitating Awareness of Movement or Changes: Reducing Compulsivity

We see that patients often regard themselves as fixed, unchanging. There are many reasons for this. They live oblivious to the moment, unable to see clearly what goes on as it takes place. If they were open to the present, they would often be aware of being in psychological pain beyond their ability to endure. As patients come closer to genuine feelings, they see that as they look at something – as they learn to objectify experience, be it a thought or a feeling – once they look at it, it subsides and changes to another thought or feeling. This is a great teaching of therapy, for it indicates the great power of the organism to heal itself. This healing arises by confronting what is taking place and seeing that we are changing moment by moment when we let be what is and do not cling to certain thoughts and feelings. As patients begin to feel more whole they are faced with the realization that they were trained to think that they could do nothing, that there was something the matter with them, and this brings into deep question their parents' past perceptions and actions. As people grow more whole they confront the illusion that their parents were truly loving, that one can get what one wants by being a good person or by working towards a goal, that one is going to be loved simply by being alive, that life is going to get better, that one is not going to get sick, or deteriorate, or die. These are illusions which are confronted as a person gains inner strength.

1.1 Change is Natural to All Forms of Life

Seeing that all things in life are constantly changing is to be a part of the world and not be isolated in it, being alive and seeing the wonder in the most ordinary things in life. Movement and change are dynamic. Fixity is static, mechanical, deadening, unreal and hopeless. We must facilitate the patient's ability to see movement and change if he is to be more who he truly, naturally is.

Movement and change can be expressed by the smallest action or difference in attitude: a new facial gesture or nuance in the voice, a different reaction to a familiar stimulus, new interests, a reference to a new name. The important thing is that where there is life, there is always some change if only we know how to see it. This chapter will address this question of facilitating awareness of change.

Psychotherapists who fail to see the whole of the person tend to focus on the pathology and not see the health of the patient, which is in part expressed in some form of changing. This focus on what is wrong is particularly prevalent in work with more disturbed patients, where so many problems are presented in one session and where the patient, because of compulsive negativity and alienation from inner experiencing, is seldom aware of movement or change taking place. For this reason it becomes important to work with this change in therapy as it occurs, so that the whole way of the patient is seen more clearly, so that the patient sees his life as not being fixed, and can thus become more hopeful. Witnessing change allows us to see a balance in what is taking place and thereby frees us from seeing only what is compulsively negative.

1.2 Denial of Change

Why do people hang on to the notion that they are not changing? This has to do with the rigid, fixed way they were treated when growing up, where attention or emotional availability were withdrawn when the patient threatened the parents' image of who he was. This often occurred when the patient felt good or experienced inner strength rooted in enthusiasm or happiness. The patient was often taught to focus on being and staying a certain way, stopping spontaneous living that would interfere with parents' fixed images of people and the world. A patient does not see change partly because he does not participate with attention in the moment, but instead lives in certain thoughts fixed on how he and others or life should be now. These images or notions have little to do with what is going on *right now*. Thus the small, subtle changes that make life full and interesting are overlooked. This produces a belief that nothing is happening, feelings of boredom, stagnation, hopelessness, anger, waste. The patient misses the joys of everyday life, the sounds we hear, the smells we smell, the wonder of seeing a smile, being touched, seeing the light change through the window.

1.3 Facilitating Awareness of Movement or Change

How do we facilitate an awareness of the movement or change

that is in fact taking place in life all the time from inside and outside, so that living is full and we are at one with it? Let us look at a session which indicates a patient's lack of awareness of change in her life as revealed in the work in psychotherapy. Let us then see how the therapist may enhance an awareness of the actual movement the patient is making.

Patient enters with her head down. She takes the pillow from one end of the analytic couch and puts it at the other end. She lies down facing me. Her legs are crossed so that I can see up her skirt. She rubs her eyes hard several times, opens them wide and stares at me. After several seconds she yawns. She says she is exhausted. Her job is exhausting her. She hates it. She speaks of one of the secretaries who she thinks is coming on to her. This woman may know she is homosexual. She thought of writing her a letter telling her she was a lesbian, but decided to wait, to feel out how the woman would respond to this since it could get her fired if it came out. She speaks of the unfairness of her boss that day. She begins to scratch her thigh. She sits up with her legs crossed.

Pt: I don't see myself getting better. Last night I was sitting in the living room studying and Kathy was sleeping, and I couldn't stand it I got so scared. I started thinking the room was full of a big witch. I had to go back to the bedroom. I was lying next to Kathy, and I couldn't look at her. I thought if I saw her face it might be wrinkled and black. Then I went over to the mirror and looked at my face, and it looked so weird. It looked disconnected from the rest of me, like a big head, the head of somebody else. I looked so unfamiliar to myself, like there was a part of me that wasn't part of my face. It was spooky.

And then I thought of you, and I got angry thinking how scared I still am coming to see you. (rubbing her eyes) I keep looking at you wondering what I see. I mean I see you, but I can't put you together. I see your face as indifferent, and I would have to say that this is how you are. You seem good at your work, you know what to say, but you don't really care. Not only about me, I think, but anyone. I get the feeling you don't really want to do this work. Maybe you'd rather be somewhere else. I know I would. Now.

I get a hell of a lot more from my astrology class, and I was thinking since my money is running out and I can go there for $10 a class, and he tells me what to do – Martin – and I believe him, and it works, what do I need this for? I can't remember getting anything from a session in months. I know I'm very sick, but this isn't my thing. I think something more mystical where there are not so much answers but signs is where I have to go. I will probably wait until I'm down to $100 though to stop.

(Takes out a cigarette) I wanted to talk about what happened Saturday 'cause I don't understand it. (Drops ashes on the floor) Oh fuck. Do you mind?

Th: (no answer)

Pt: Well, if you don't, I don't. That pisses the shit out of me.

Th: What's that?

Pt: What am I supposed to do, get a vacuum cleaner? The ashtray is full of butts. That isn't exactly appealing. (leaning over to get the ashtray)

Anyway . . . Saturday this thing happened. Kathy asked me to go to these people's house, this couple. I met them before. I said I would go, and then I just sat at the kitchen table. I didn't get dressed. I was getting madder and madder.

So when she came through I got up and said I wasn't going. She started screaming that I was always doing this to her. I said that I had pains in my back, which I did. She said I was destroying all the other relationships she had because these are her friends. And they are her friends, I mean they're crazy about her like everybody is. She's the big star. So I was furious, and then I started to hold my head, and I was crying, just putting my head on the table and crying. She walked out and left me alone.

But the crazy thing was that I didn't especially care. I was just really crying. Then I started to smoke and I got stoned. When she got home I was smashed. I called her names, but I didn't care about what I was saying 'cause I wasn't feeling anything. I went to sleep on the couch watching this movie . . .

Oh . . . when is all this shit gonna end? That's what I mean. We live together but we didn't get closer. We keep having the same crap, and I get discouraged. I don't change the ways I act, pretending to be sick all the time when really I'm jealous 'cause they like her more, and the same shit. So Martin would say your moon is in Jupiter and so cool it. He would tell me what to do . . . he would say that I should not have agreed to go. Okay. You hear all this. What do you say?

This session illustrates some common features of how patients deny change. First, the patient is not aware of how she is able to contain her anxiety when she sits with her feelings on Saturday, or does not reveal in the office that she is a lesbian. She does not see how she is more involved with me, less avoiding her own feelings of confusion, interest and sadness. She does not see her perception of herself and me as getting clearer as she looks in the mirror. She does not respect her increased emotional participation in her own therapy, which is revealed by saying at one point, "I wanted to talk about what happened Saturday." In the past this patient had no sense of wanting to talk *to me* about anything. This is indeed a change. Instead, this patient remains compulsively attached to the negative notion that "nothing is changing." The patient is not aware that in her associations she thinks of me when she is scared in her apartment and that this indicates a deepening connection between us. After one year of work she is talking of leaving therapy, while the real struggle is with her staying and getting closer to herself and to me. She is changing in her relationship with me as observed in her stating that she wanted to talk about Saturday, with a more genuine affect in this wanting. This patient is moving in her process of differentiating to where she is beginning to struggle with the question of who she is, as is evidenced by her looking in the mirror and seeing herself and me as separate.

Now after one year, she can feel and say that there is "a part of *me* that is not my face." She is beginning to see the therapist as separate from her, she is more involved *with* the therapist, at times listening to me, and now, as a major change, wanting to talk with *her* therapist. These are key changes — for this patient to be interested in who she is, to want to talk with the therapist, and to be able to listen. The patient is aware of none of these changes.

As the patient begins to move closer to herself and the therapist, she moves into the process that Winncott describes in his article, "The Use of the Object."[1] The patient now begins to try to destroy the treatment to see if the therapist can remain free of her ways of omnipotent control, can survive her attempts at destructiveness in a way which is qualitatively not retaliatory or rejecting. This is what her own mother could not do — she could not survive the patient's anxiety, anger and moves to control. It is essential for the therapist to recognize and appreciate the movement as this patient is so disconnected and denying of it. Without seeing change we are easily defeated by the patient's words, which often speak of nothing happening. These words represent the need of parents, and symbolize a clinging to the past.

Being compulsively negative, this patient feels that things are not changing in positive ways in the treatment. She is habitually aware of what is wrong, what is the problem, what is missing in her life. The therapist, in order to enhance an awareness of the larger whole of what is taking place, looks for and recognizes the *movement* in the work that the patient misses. The therapist balances the fixity and compulsive vision by *working with and inquiring into those processes which are not fixed*. The therapist looks at what is forming, not stuck. Thus the therapist balances what is healthy and unhealthy and serves as a balancing force with the patient. The patient is unbalanced only in his compulsive focus on what is the matter.

This patient misses how she is changing in life as it is taking place. The therapist listens and observes where there is something new going on in the session. Knowing that movement is natural to all forms in nature, knowing that the blockage to seeing movement creates the patient's hopelessness, helplessness, the therapist brings the movement to the attention of the patient by inquiring into those areas where there has been or is in the session actual change that represents the growth of the patient. The therapist opens up for inquiry only what she is in actuality creating that is new in her life. The therapist works where she has or is able to master or think or feel something new, in either the session or the content reported. This movement will be underlined with clarification, with inquiry, with confrontation, interpretation, reflection of its denial, etc. The therapist thus intervenes *where* there is movement and change and does not inquire into where the inner processes are most compulsive or fixed as the patient cannot do anything to change these compulsive processes. As the patient is more whole, feels more substantial, these fixed ways will open up, loosen, and can then be explored.

In this session Lynn appears to be talking of leaving the treatment. She denies her own changes and experiences "having the same crap," while in fact, her life is changing considerably. She is currently living in the experience of feeling closer to her roommate than before, but she has forgotten this. She is also affectively letting in more of the therapist's presence, which she couldn't do at the beginning of the work. She appeared to be talking to herself much of the time for six months, and is now clearly including the therapist in her world. The therapist sees change as the patient is discovering externality itself, with the therapist now felt as a person in reality.

Winnicott says the patient must try to destroy the therapist as a way to create health: "If it is in an analysis that these matters are taking place, then the analyst, the analytic technique, and the analytic setting all come in as surviving or not surviving the patient's destructive attacks. This destructive activity is the patient's attempt to place the anlayst outside the area of omnipotent control, that is, out in the world. . . . Without the experience of maximum destructiveness the subject never places the analyst outside and therefore can never do more than experience a kind of self-analysis, using the analyst as a projection of a part of the self." (Winnicott, *Playing and Realty*, "The Use of the Object").[2] Lynn's attempts to destroy the meaning of the therapeutic work and her threats to leave can be seen as a fear of changing and a denial of that change as well as the need to try to destroy the therapist in that process as Winnicott describes.

Important work and change are going on in the relationship with this patient. The patient is creating external reality as she finds out if I can survive her moves to control me, as she controlled so many others by stating constant dissatisfaction and threatening to leave. Having seen the movement and seen the patient getting more involved with me, I hear her talking about moving to greater differentiation. I am aware that the patient is more involved in talking to me. And I want to convey that it is important for her to talk to me, that I am taking on more meaning for her as she sees more of me, thus more of herself. I keep this change in pattern of relating in mind and wonder how to underline it in what I say. The patient is continually living out, acting out her own fear of loss by leaving, threatening to abandon, fearing feeling into what it would mean to face what is actually movement – *staying* – and the greater wholeness and connection that comes from staying, staying with her lover, with me, with her own feelings. *Seeing all this, knowing this, I feel quite hopeful and do not work at the level of the patient's words:* "the same crap." Rather, I work within the context of the patient's actions.

Let us look more closely at this patient.

Lynn has come twice weekly for over a year. Originally chaotic and frightened about her lover's leaving, not having much direction, wanting to write and not being able to, this patient left job after job in anger, or was fired for her nasty behavior. She was sexually promiscuous, and would at times spend weekends sleeping with several different people she had picked up in bars. When anxious she would walk around her apartment building knocking on people's doors, or space out, or go to bars to find casual sex. She was usually furious with one person or another. She complained of numerous psychosomatic complaints and was involved in a deeply dependent relationship with her mother. She called her mother several times a day, and was often afraid she was dying of cancer.

Since treatment began the patient has lived with a woman she feels for, although she often "cheats" on her. She has been working on a master's in history and has managed to stay in school despite endless arrangements for extensions, missing classes, and generally angry behavior with teachers. Of late she has been complaining more and more of the treatment not being what she feels she needs. She is looking at me more in sessions, sometimes listening to what I say. She often sits on the couch facing me, but now she opens her legs more. It does not strike me as seductive, but shows me that she is a bit more relaxed. She begins by staring at me; this may last several seconds and is usually intense. She appears to be seeing me more. It has the feel of one person looking at another as outside, not needing me to merge with her – which I had felt at the beginning when she seemed to need to suck me in as her words poured out, non-stop, enveloping me.

It is clear to me that in this session the patient is struggling with and talking over what has been a major issue for her in her life: the containment of anxiety. She is now able to act in her own behalf: she does not write the letter to the secretary at work telling her she is a homosexual. She might have done this up until this point. We have talked about her need to do things right away, how come she feels she can't wait, how it feels to have to do things even when they backfire, how some things do backfire, what it might be to wait, what is worth waiting for, etc. We have gone over this and now the patient does wait. *But she does not own it, she does not experience this as movement or change, or as meaningful.* But I recognize and appreciate it. In seeing this, I can enable the patient further to differentiate, for in essence I give needed recognition of change and freedom to change by respecting it. I also have a new image of Lynn. By gaining the therapist's recognition, Lynn is given unspoken permission to grow, to change. Yet the patient is aware of almost nothing of this.

In order to decide how to intervene, I ask myself: *What is this patient struggling with in her life, in this session. What is genuinely the movement in her life, what is changing*? I see a struggle with containing her anxiety, and I also see her struggling to reveal to me, and to keep for herself, and struggling with the question of "Who am I?" She looks in the mirror to gain a clearer sense of herself. She uses me as a mirror. She moves towards a new image of herself. Throughout this session the patient struggles with the question of her old ideas of herself, of how others should treat her, all of which are based on her conditioned ideas from childhood. Since some people are not treating her in the expected way, she is feeling anxiety which arises from being in the unknown, which stretches beyond the confines of her past. The patient is struggling with new concepts, old concepts of who she is; she is looking more at who she is right now. *All these struggles are movement into new ways of being, thinking, feeling, living – of which the patient is unaware.* The therapist sees all this movement and, when it seems right, will articulate these processes over time.

To see what the patient is struggling with is to see where there is movement when the words spoken indicate that there is no movement.

As this patient moves to see herself in the mirror, she sees that she is disconnected from the whole of herself "like a big head." She feels she has "somebody else's head," which might be a metaphor for what it is to imitate someone and not to have a consistent internal image of who she is. She begins to feel unfamiliar to herself as many new things emerge in her life. The patient says that not only is she looking at herself, seeing that there are distortions in her inner vision, but she also says, "I keep looking at you, wondering what I see . . . I can't put you together." The patient is moving to see herself and the other person as separate and feels the strangeness of both, whereas prior to treatment she had not reflected on much of anything in the world.

Now things begin to be differentiated and she has some control over creating her life. She chooses not to tell the people at work she is a lesbian. She chooses to stay home on Saturday. In this session, the patient is moving to express the *new ways of seeing herself* and the *old ways of seeing herself.* As she begins to look and to "wonder what I see," she sees the astrology teacher, who may be a symbol of giving and what she needs from her therapy and her life, "not so much answers but signs." She is struggling to read the signs outside of herself and to interact with them. She does need signs of what is going on as she has always read magically into things from inside her own head.

Looking in the mirror permits a new aspect of herself to emerge. "There is a part of me that wasn't part of my face." This suggests a firmer grounding, a more substantial sense of something inside felt as "a part of me." It is a new, changing, more whole "me." A new image of herself on a more positive note is suggested when she says "I get things from astrology." She has seldom felt that she gets anything from anything, except the study of history. The description of her crying on Saturday represents change or movement for after her lover left, she said that she "didn't especially care . . . I was just really crying." In the past Lynn would have been suffused with rage at being left; she would merely have smoked grass, had masochistic fantasies, and watched TV. The crying is an indication that she was more with herself, with her feelings on Saturday, not escaping them. This crying was described as "the crazy thing," suggesting that *it was a new kind of crying, a new way of living in her pain*, being more with herself *as is*, being sad . . . not running from it. She is getting to know her actuality in her therapy and is less enraged, less compulsive as she lets herself be herself without avoidance. Some old ways of seeing herself come out in this session, expressed as exhausted, sick, indifferent, a big witch, mad, weird, homosexual, angry, pissed, jealous.

This session expresses the movement of a person being more with herself as she is and not escaping: *as Lynn is more able to be more with herself, she can be a bit closer to others*. Now the other person she is closer to is me. I feel this in the session, but also, *for the first time, the patient indicates that she wanted to talk to me*. It is rather subtly articulated in this way and quickly passed over. Unless the therapist is listening and observing closely for movement and change, it might be missed. Lynn says, "I wanted to talk about what happened Saturday 'cause I don't understand it." I hear that statement this way: "I wanted to talk *to you* (these words were omitted in her statement) about what happened Saturday . . ." This is moving closer to me than before when it often seemed that I was hardly in the room with her at all as she didn't listen much to me. The patient also suggests that she is interested in understanding some of her actions, instead of complaining about her lover's abuse, which had formerly been her exclusive focus.

What we see here is considerable movement towards figuring out who she is, who I am, towards being with herself, getting interested in her inner processes, really crying for unknown reasons, beginning to feel for herself, seeing herself more in actuality, containing anxiety, making actual effort towards some goal-oriented thinking in her studies. Now here is how the patient puts this movement: "When is all this shit gonna end? We live together but we don't get closer. We keep having the same crap, and I get discouraged. *I don't change the ways I act . . . and the same shit*." For the patient who is unaware of the changes, it is "the same shit."

The question for the therapist is how to open up inquiry where there has been actual movement in the session. I emphasize her wanting to talk to me on Saturday. *I let her know in my response that I heard her wanting to talk to me, thinking of me out of the session. I underline the movement simply by referring to it.* I do not explore it yet, but appreciate the lessening of her need to deny my existence. *I will also inquire into this "really crying," as the feel of it is more genuine than much of her behavior.*

As my intervention I say to her, "You say you wanted to talk *to me* about what happened on Saturday. Tell me about when you were just really crying." She then said that she felt sad and didn't know why; it was something about how much she had been alone as a kid and how scared she felt being alone the night before. There was something new here that she didn't understand. I asked her to say more about this being alone, and she remembered times waiting for her mother to come home and feeling lonely, and wanting to hug her mother, but for reasons she didn't understand, she usually ended up screaming or fighting. We talked of how she learned to stop this wanting to hug, to be close, and how this goes on now. She talked of wanting to hug Kathy a lot, but had to push it down. We talked of her need for hugging and the naturalness of it.

There was no mention of leaving anymore this time. There was no mention at all of wanting to talk to me. *But we had both heard it and knew it was there in our relationship now*, a form of movement to greater trust, which is threatening as well as relieving to this patient.

How can I bring the movement and change I see to the attention of the patient? I intervene in the session with some technique of psychotherapy, be it interpretation, clarification, confrontation, inquiry where there is actual change. Here there were many choices. In this session I choose to focus on two forms of change: her wish to use my help and her being with her own more genuine feelings (in crying) and not avoiding them. I reflect her wish to talk and inquire into the change in her being able to stay with her own experiencing. I can make other choices but I think the most fruitful areas are the change in our relationship and her being with her own experiencing of inner pain. My question and my statement focus on where she showed movement, which enable her to feel more aware of her own changing process and increase her sense of hope.

I facilitate awareness of change *by working in the session where there is some actual movement.* Once one learns to see movement and change, one sees them in every session.

If I had said to this particular patient that there was considerable evidence that we do have a relationship, articulated the evidence, and talked about her need to deny this, I think she would have felt imposed on since her mother was always telling her what was going on with her. The implication there was that Lynn was very sick and needed caring for, or that her mother was about to collapse and Lynn had to pick up the slack caused by her mother's depression. With another patient it might have been helpful to make more interpretations but not with this particular

patient, who most often responded to interpretive interventions as if I
didn't understand her at all, and then with considerably disruptive feelings.

Pathology represents the compulsive, the fixed in the patient. Where
the patient is most repetitive and fixed in his way of thinking is often
where the beginning therapist makes the most effort. One way to work to
facilitate greater awareness of movement and change is to work outside
the fragment which is most compulsive, that is, *at the growing edge* of
the patient. This relates to the question in treatment of *where to intervene*.

1.4 Working at the Growing Edge

People have many difficulties when they come into therapy. A few of the
common ones are: low self-esteem, a dim sense of identity, difficulty with
long-range, goal-directed thinking, frustration over goals, tension around
others, feeling impelled to be the way other people want them to be, a
vague sense of what is taking place outside or inside at the present
moment, a feeling of not being right, being isolated from others, of losing
control, growing angry or withdrawing, a sense of incompleteness and
unhappiness.

In the beginning of treatment we hear and see people who are unable
to live in the presence of another person without fear, who break up
relationships when they are not flattered, who have spent a lifetime
hearing what is wrong with them, or hearing how they have failed to be
what they should be. People come to us with a profound inner vulnerability to the ideas of others as well as a fear of being influenced. We see
people who are easily injured, genuinely fearful, and consumed with rage.
Often people do not know what they personally think, or feel, or want.
They habitually do what their mothers and fathers wanted them to do, or
what mother and father substitutes (lovers, friends, etc.) want them to do.
They have little sense of themselves as they are unable to be in relationships
long enough to tolerate feedback which does not coincide with their own
opinion of themselves. They are unable to learn anything new about themselves, cannot stand alone if necessary, or live with their own resources.

The patient comes to us in defeat, not believing that anything can really
help, but at the same time magically believing that after he tells us about
himself we will do something to make it better. The patient has usually
had little experience of being allowed the freedom to think or feel originally or spontaneously. Most of what he says is conditioned by what others
have wanted from him. He is in an internal state of fearing to be kicked
out, fearing he is boring, fearing that we cannot care about him, fearing
having to make effort, feeling that he cannot do what he wants, cannot be

any way be wants to be, and be respected as a fellow human; he is confused about what he can do in life and more confused about what he wants to do — unable to set priorities, unable to give anything up — thinking that he can some day accomplish everything, give up nothing. The patient is angry and disappointed with others on many counts and at times is afraid this anger and sadness will get out of control. There is fear of being in new situations and in some way found out to be incompetent. There is fear of other people, feeling not a part of life, unwanted by others.

In this internal condition, the patient can do little to change, cannot take the new actions necessary to resolve the problems he brings to us in treatment to solve. The patient asks the therapist to change his life's most deeply conditioned patterns — to help him leave him, to find out what he wants to do, to get him interested in things, to allow him to be more deeply involved with people, to help him find someone to love, etc. Until the patient feels stronger inwardly, more accepting of himself, less ruled by past notions, clearer as to what he wants and who he is, he cannot make the efforts required to attain the changes he seeks, for the changes mean changing the patterns he has been trained to cling to most all of his life. The person must begin to feel something good and natural or authentic or genuine in himself before he can feel that there is any reason to think he can actually hope for change. He must begin to look within to discover he has his own point of view before knowing he can create his own fate rather than demanding that change come from others. He must feel self-esteem based on actual mastery and change before he can live with the anxiety demanded by putting himself into new situations. Before he can look at pain inside of himself, difficulties inside himself, he must feel that he is inwardly strong enough to bear with this pain and not avoid it. *No person can change until he can look at who he is in fact.*

In order to change, a person must see that what is happening is related to how he is acting. Then he must see which ways of behaving or being create his troubles. Then he must give them up. This is difficult for the healthiest person to do, for it means letting go of all that we have learned in the past, giving up our cherished notions of life, of the ways in which we have been conditioned to act, of the false security our compulsive behavior gives, deluding us into thinking that we are always right or always wrong — depending on the way our conditioning went. We can realize when we have maintained an interest that to find an interest, then to make the effort that goes with exploring the interest, to go with all the difficulties that accompany involvement in an interest, then in working with and enduring the struggles the interest will entail, to tolerate the hurts, doubts, desires for other things, to make the personal sacrifices an interest demands, to exert discipline and rigor, is often difficult for the strongest individual. Yet the patient, with little connection to the struggle involved, comes in saying, "I'm not interested in anything. I want to get interested. I want to find an interest." It is difficult for the most integrated person to stay in a relationship at certain points, to stay close with another, to be able to leave one's family and give up parental notions, to get a divorce, to change jobs, to make sacrifices for work — yet these are some things the patient wants or expects as he begins treatment. He talks of them endlessly, as if talking would make it easy. An enraged patient wants her head pains to go away. She is not even aware that she is angry. Although she talks of her pain, she runs from experiencing it. She disconnects from her anger as soon as it comes up in her. We listen to these compulsive complaints and see that although they are obsessively talked about, thought about, the patient is not able to carry out the actions required to achieve the consequences he speaks of until he is more aware of who he is *in fact*, and until he has a substantially more positive self-concept based on actual mastery.

The most deeply conditioned, compulsive patterns are those which are most difficult to give up, and which present the most difficulty to the patient. This is the area of greatest pathology. These compulsive patterns are usually presented as the first order for solution by the patient. It is because the patient cannot yet move on these deeply conditioned matters that he feels stuck, fixed, immobile. Compulsivity is synonymous with illness. The sicker the person, the more compulsive he is. This is seen in the ritualistic behavior of the schizophrenic person who keeps repeating the same action over and over. The healthier the person, the more spontaneous, the more free he is to be any way he chooses.

The behavior that is most compulsive, repetitive, is the most deeply conditioned and the most difficult for the patient to change. For this reason we want to begin to work in the area of least compulsivity, which is the area in the session where the patient is most open, least compulsive, so that the patient can feel stronger, more hopeful than if he worked on the most intractable areas. The therapist does not get stuck in what the patient most compulsively describes as needing "fixing," for the therapist has the wisdom to be patient, knows that the patient is not ready for certain choices, and has faith that in a calm, abiding, free environment, where the patient is given the space to be who he is without labels, the patient will shed the ignorance of who he is in fact. The therapist does not open up for inquiry that which the patient can do nothing about. The therapist's skillful assessment lies in deciding what the patient can work on fruitfully. The therapist intervenes and opens up for further exploration and inquiry *what the patient has actually been able to do something about, where the patient has shown some mastery, where there is some positive feeling present, where there is some actual interest and involvement no matter how small. The therapist works outside the circle of greatest compulsivity, at the growing edge where there is something new, something that is emerging which is more positive and whole, some incipient process or behavior, some new behavior described or observed in the session, anything outside of conditioned, destructive, repetitive ways of behaving.*

Knowing that it always appears, the therapist listens for the edge of growth in each session. It emerges, even in the most compulsively negative patients who seem to complain about the same thing week after week. There is always movement, always something new and more whole, because the human organism is always in flux so that what is verbally presented as "the same" is never the same. The therapist's skill is being able to hear or see or feel the movement in the session, the edge of growth, the small transformation, the shifts, the newness each time the person arrives. We intervene to bring this movement to the patient's greater awareness without false reassurance by working in the session where there is some actual growth. This work at the growing edge enables the patient to begin to recognize movement and to reduce the sense of internal rigidity and hopelessness about change.

In each person's life there are places where there is more or less compulsivity. With one's spouse, for example, one may find oneself endlessly thinking and doing the same sorts of things. However, when we are with a certain friend we may feel a different way, be different to some extent. We may find ourselves totally bored and afraid of how nothing interests us and then we find that when we wash the dishes, the feel of the warm soapy water is calming, nice, and we like to wash dishes. In every person's life there are spaces, places which are more open, relationships which are more open, moments with oneself where one is temporarily open to life's possibilities.

The therapist would open up for exploration any behavior or content in the session which is new and reflects greater participation in life, increased realization of options or spontaneity, new thoughts, new ways of feeling or seeing oneself, others, the therapist. We are thus particularly interested in these moments in the session:

1) where there is participation in creating new forms in the session;
2) where the patient participates in a more engaged way in the session;
3) where the involvement occurs in the session.

Most therapists think they should work on the pathology, which is to explore with the patient what he can do nothing about at that moment in time. Let us look at a clinical example of a therapist who did not work at the growing edge but focused on the problem the patient presented as most pressing, not aware of how this would deepen the despair and compulsivity of the patient.

A young man who has always been in and out of relationships with women has formed a relationship with a woman. He is living in her apartment along with her mother. The two women feed and care for the man, who has left his own alcoholic father and abusive mother for this living arrangement. The man comes from a family of alcoholics. He has an older brother in prison on a drug charge. His mother has high expectations for him since he is the only family member to attend college. He feels hopeless about his future and enters treatment complaining of premature ejaculation.

Although he is ordinarily hostile, negative, and feeling defeated about his future, in this eighth session the therapist notes a calmer, less hostile affect. The session begins with this man discussing how he has been able to stop smoking because he is worried about his health. The therapist does not go into this. His next train of association is how on the way to the session he ran into a girl he knew from school and thought was nice. He describes being glad to see her. The therapist does not explore what he likes about this girl or what kind of relationship they had, although she notes that his manner is positive, a change from his usual sour mood. He then begins to compare this girl to his current girlfriend. He is feeling that he should be working or looking for a job. They have trouble with sex. There is a pause.

The therapist suggests that they talk more about his sexual problem. He goes on to describe how he should leave his girlfriend, look for another girl, but he can't. He is humiliated by his inability to perform. What follows is a great deal of self-hate and compulsive talk about how he can't have good sex. The patient leaves the session clear that he hates himself for his massive dependency needs and sexual inadequacy.

What has the therapist done to help? She has brought out massive self-hate in areas where the patient can currently do nothing to change them. What he *can do* the therapist overlooks and does not open up with inquiry. It would have been helpful to explore how it felt for him to stop smoking, specifically to go into how he managed to give this up, what he saw as new experiences coming out of it, and perhaps to make a statement as to how he is more connected with his bodily sensations than he used to be, how he now wants to feel stronger, and has done something about this.

This non-holistic therapist sees her work as being to focus on problems — even though she knows that this man is so inwardly confused about who he is and what he wants, that he is inert. She knows that he clings to his girlfriend as he would to anyone who would tell him what to do or provide the external structure that he is so lacking internally. She knows that he has a low self-esteem and feels that he can do nothing about his life even though he is 26 years old. She knows his aspirations do not conform to his abilities.

Yet she will work on what he cannot do anything about, she will focus on the most compulsive pathology: his premature ejaculation in sex. She misses exploring where processes of movement and incipient health are emerging. These holistic processes would be a sufficiently steady foundation on which to build new inner strength. But this therapist, like most beginning therapists, will focus on what is the matter. She does not understand that her patient has such a dim sense of who he is that he cannot possibly change the nature of his dependency needs until he has been helped to feel he can do something on his own, until he feels more aware of what he wants, thinks, feels, imagines.

In this session he tells us that something comes from inside of him; it is this: *he stopped smoking; he likes this girl from school.* For the patient so isolated from people and from his own experiences, this is a feeling state that could helpfully be explored so that he can own the experience, so that it can become a new aspect of his self-image.

As treatment begins, we work so that the patient will and can eventually have the inner strength to take action on the issues he complains about: premature ejaculation, finding a job, leaving home. Once treatment has come to where the patient has more trust in us, more faith in himself, then we can begin to look more fruitfully at the more compulsive patterns of living. Before this there must be some sense of change within the person, some sense of being able to affect his own fate.

In the course of this session the patient mentions that his girlfriend has a car and that her house is nice and clean. Both of these facts are important to the patient. In neither instance does the therapist explore these areas. At one point in this session the patient says, "I never used to stay with one girl because of my sexual difficulties. I would go out a few times and then have to end the relationship because I felt bad about my 'performance.' " Here the therapist is hearing that this current relationship gives the patient something that allows him to stay in it. She does not interpret this, nor does she mention that he is able to be closer to someone now and ask why this may be happening. This is a major area of movement in the patient's life; to bring it to the patient's attention would have led him to see that he is changing. The therapist does not bring this up.

Instead, as the patient mentions staying with this girl, she replies, "What is it you feel about your sexual performance?" He goes on to say that this has always been hard for him to talk about and that he has never told anyone how he has had premature ejaculation. Instead of asking how it is for him to tell her, acknowledging that he is sharing more with her than with anyone in his life, the therapist asks the patient to describe when he has had this sexual problem before, totally overlooking the interpersonal aspect of sharing, revealing, opening up in the therapeutic relationship. The patient begins to talk of all his miserable failures in the past, and uses the word "pressure" in describing how he feels in sex. The therapist asks for more associations of his experience with being "pressured." The patient begins to sigh and at the end of the session appears depressed.

In this session there were many edges of growth outside the circle of compulsive negativity: stopping smoking, meeting a girl he likes, feeling good to see her, liking having a car in his life, responding to the orderliness of his girlfriend's house, being able to stay in a relationship for the first time in his life despite sexual difficulties, revealing to the therapist in a way he has never talked to anyone before. None of these was opened up for exploration so that the patient could see that movement and change are happening in his life, that life is opening up. Instead, at the end of the session the patient feels a sense of failure because of his sexual difficulty, which is the fragment by which he defines himself and which is his presenting complaint.

The therapist is convinced that her work is to focus on the patient's conflicts and pathology. She doesn't see that in order to make changes here, the patient must first feel better about himself. Feeling better must be connected with who he genuinely is, and in this session there is a lot of evidence for exploration to facilitate awareness of movement. This man is dependent because he feels that there is little going on inside himself; he feels worthless and empty. The therapist could help him see that he is inwardly alive and moving by underlining his actual inner movement, change in the form of new ability to stay in a relationship, new interests. These are actual accomplishments. He would then eventually begin to feel hopeful about being able to change what he considers problem areas.

Every day in supervision I see therapists missing what the patient has been able to do, focusing on what is wrong, working in the deepest pathology where the patient is not yet strong enough to make changes. The therapist all too often works only with what is stuck.

A man in his forties comes in very angry. He has been out of work and is hard on himself about not being able to find work. He has spent much of his life fighting with or being angry with his wife, yet he is unable to leave her. He feels nobody wants him, he is a failure, and he is bitter and nasty at work. He has few friends and alienates his son with his jealous rages about his son's accomplishments.

In this session he describes how his wife gave him a surprise birthday party over the weekend after he had asked her not to make a party because they had little money. He says everyone but him had fun. He was furious. He says lightly that the party cost X and that he wanted to buy an amplifier instead of giving a party. He says that he has the amplifier picked out. He goes on to condemn his wife. The therapist states, "You feel that your wife doesn't understand you – or listen to you." The man spends the rest of the session compulsively complaining that it wouldn't matter if he was alive or dead since no one hears him, etc.

Here the therapist did not hear the *growing edge* for this man, which was knowing what he wanted: an amplifier. She might have said, "You certainly knew what you wanted." What is movement here is that this usually numb man knew and wanted something. To underline this moving process, the therapist might have said, "There is something new going on here for you with the clarity of knowing what you wanted," or simply, "I hear all this, but I also hear that you are clear in knowing what you want." This would convey that he is inwardly experiencing something: that is, wanting. I would not yet make a statement about his inability to assert this want more directly because he is not yet able to do this.

We sometimes work with patients who have little inner experience connected with what they do, and when they actually participate in something meaningful, they disconnect from it quickly since it arouses longing or conflict or anxiety to move outside the usual certainty of negative compulsive behavior. Here is an example from supervision of a therapist missing the healthy movement and not working with it.

A chaotic, disorganized patient in her early twenties constantly rearranges the therapist's room in small ways, although she does not know why. It seems that she is looking for greater internal comfort and knows how to effect that only by changing what is outside. There is continual idealizing and degrading of the therapist. There is constant talk of the therapist's power over her, hateful fighting over much of what the therapist says. The patient loses one job after another, thrashes around in the office for one year, often complaining that nothing is happening, she doesn't know why she comes.

One day she brings a small pocket knife to the session, saying that she often plays with this at home, studying it, thinking of ramming it into her wrists, that there is nothing she can do well in life. She wants to ram it into a corkboard on the wall of the therapist's office. The therapist tries to explore this, but the patient screams, "Let me do what I want. Let me do what I want. I can't do anything I want." The patient calms down and says viciously, "I want to tear your walls down so that you'll not have any office and you'll have to grovel on the street like me from job to job. See, you mother fucker? Now do you get it?" The patient gets up and walks out. The therapist feels completely exhausted.

In the next session, the patient takes out the pocket knife and sits cleaning her nails. At one point the knife slips and she cuts her finger a bit. She begins to hold it, to suck on it, and then suddenly sobs. She says, "I don't know what I am doing with myself. I feel confused all the time. I don't want to hurt myself . . . I didn't mean to do that . . . oh, oh . . . " She is crying and begins to hold her head in her hands. The therapist gets up and asks the patient if she wants a bandage. The patient says softly, "No." The therapist says, "I'll get it if you want." The patient is still crying and does not respond.

The therapist leaves the room, returns with a bandaid. The patient then jumps up screaming, "Why don't you leave me alone . . . I didn't ask for that. Get the hell out of here," etc. The patient leaves the session, screaming, and the therapist calls her that evening, afraid that the patient may harm herself.

In this session, what is new, outside the circle of compulsivity, is the girl's beginning sense of her own suffering; for the first time she begins to feel and own her own confusion. She says, "I don't know what I am doing with myself – I feel confused all the time. I didn't want to hurt myself . . . I didn't mean to do that." Here there is some incipient sense of compassion, but the therapist does not stay with this. The therapist, out of her own anxiety at seeing the deep sadness and terror of this patient, becomes concrete and cuts off the emotional experiencing of the patient. There is a genuine loss of empathy as the *growing edge of movement is overlooked* by the therapist because of her anxiety at the depth of the patient's anger. At some level the patient knows she isn't being heard.

After letting her be with herself, letting her cry, being with her, letting her work on her own, I would acknowledge the movement and say, "You say you don't want to hurt yourself . . . " This is what is new, what is change, what is movement, what is actual healing at the moment it is being created. I see it, I appreciate it, I empathize with the patient's suffering at her compulsive self-destructiveness, and let her resonate with her own insight into this – then I underline what has in fact changed in her view of herself in the way she lives.

*   *   *

A woman with two children is often "despairing" in the evening after work, she says. She sees no purpose to her life at those times. She smokes, paints the apartment constantly, yells at her children, often falls asleep before making dinner. She describes going into one child's room and seeing his clothes all over the floor. She goes over to him and puts her hand on his shoulder and then begins to scream. I listen to the chaos of the rest of the evening, and remember the new gesture of putting her hand on his shoulder. This woman did calm down a moment, did see something other than the mess of things. I inquire to find out what this woman experienced in putting her hand on her son's shoulder, what she might have been saying with this gesture. At the end of the session, both patient and therapist were hearing movement in her emerging tenderness for her son.

*   *   *

A young man who was poor, raised in a family where the father was seldom home with many older brothers and a sick mother, describes how he got into another fight on the way to the therapist's office. He begins to talk about how his father was sick all the time and didn't teach him to fight, but his brothers did. There is much talk of fighting with many people.

He then talks of a movie he saw last weekend where "there is this guy in it who was a terrific person, an old guy and whom all the kids in the town loved." The therapist says, "A father type. The kind of father you might have liked to have." The patient says "Yeah" and then goes into talking of how his father gave him nothing so that he is now nothing . . .

What is important here is that the young man identifies with this kind person in the movie, that he recognizes kindness when he sees it, which means that he knows it from within himself. I might say directly to the patient, "In order to see this man's kidness you must have known this in yourself," or "Do you feel in touch with what there is inside you similar to the man in the movie?" If, however, I make an interpretation at this point, the patient would not be given a chance to explore his own particular response to this kind, older man — to find out more about his own feeling towards this man, what he liked, what he saw, what he responded to, his thoughts about this kind of person, what else. In a more open exploration, the patient could make connections from inside himself leading to a sense of movement from fixed notions of himself.

Now let us look at an example where movement at the growing edge was worked with in treatment. I saw this patient for eight months before he left for graduate school. My interventions emphasized more holistic living as it emerged in our work, as well as articulating and inquiring where I saw him changing and connecting. Throughout our work I was careful to intervene where there was movement, i.e., where the patient was actually able to change his habitual behavior.

1.4.1 Examples of working with the movement

The patient began his initial interview by telling me that he was a psychology major in his senior year at a City college. He had a 3.7 index, all A's in his psychology courses, and was into dope: "LSD and grass." I felt anxious about him immediately, in part as a result of his opening move, which was to push his chair containing his 6'3" body with his shirt opened to the waist to a position about twelve inches from my chair. When I asked him what brought him to therapy at this time, he said, "I can't urinate in public toilets. But I can't urinate any place where I think people can hear me. I can't stand to make that noise. This means in my house, my mother has to be at least two rooms away. And the same with Jane, my girlfriend, and David, my friend. They both know about my problem." He went on to say that this problem had persisted since grade school, but then he could urinate when he went home for lunch. In high school, he held his urine all day, suffering acute discomfort, and the dread that he wouldn't be able to "hold it in." He said that his problem bothered him a lot now since he had begun to value his body more since tripping, to like it's being big and manly, and since he had a girlfriend who is so free. Although Jane is understanding of his hang-up, he has begun to feel ashamed of such a "stupid hang-up." He describes himself as coming on as "cool" to other people, and believing that he cons people.

I note the high pitch of his voice, his constant smiling, and the trembling of his hands. He tells me that it has only been in the last couple of years that he has begun to move out of his family into a more active social life. Before that, most of his time was taken up either with studying or playing basketball. Six months ago, he bought a used car with money he had earned working summers in a law firm library, and since then he went for rides, to rock concerts, to some parties, and enjoyed it all thoroughly.

Moving into the world has made his symptom more difficult for him, he says. Every time he goes to a party he is obsessed with fear that he will have to urinate and won't be able to find a toilet at a safe distance from the people there. He describes his best friend David, a friend since high school, laughing at his symptom. David walks around naked all the time, supplies him with acid, and thinks "body hang-ups are stupid."

When I ask about the frequency of the dope and tripping, he states that he trips at least once a month on acid, smokes pot several times a week, and feels he is Jesus Christ when on acid. He says people have told him that he looks like Jesus, and indeed, the long beard, waist-length hair, and beautiful hands are similar, but his small and terrified dark eyes are the antithesis of openness and love.

He mentions that he came from Israel to America at age 7 with his mother, father, and older sister. They lived in a small rural community in a house in Israel and his parents had many friends there. He does not know exactly why his father decided to come to New York; he thinks it was to make more money since he is a construction worker and had heard of the high pay scale in New York. He states spontaneously that his father has a second-grade education, cannot write English, and that his mother finished the fifth grade.

He states that the change from Israel to the States was radical: His family moved from a house near the park into a four-room apartment in a low-income Bronx project where they have lived ever since. His mother is frightened in New York, didn't allow Joe to play outside, repeated rumors that people regularly got killed on the streets. His mother carefully watched over his life, insisted that he come straight home from school every day.

His father found work readily as "he is a bull of a man, 6'3" and strong as an ox." Joe expresses contempt for his father's never learning to write English, and for his own compliance in taking care of all his father's written affairs.

He remembers being ashamed of not knowing the language when he arrived, being asked his first day in second grade to write an essay in class, and feeling terrified to turn in the blank page. No one had told the school staff that he didn't know any English. He speaks of his family's current isolation, his own feelings of being left out and unhappy until he could speak some English, his family's never going into a restaurant, his mother's having no friends, and his own social isolation aside from his friend David, until recently.

Glowingly he speaks of the happy times he recalled in Israel, running freely, playing games, having friends. He then says with uncontrollable laughter, "I guess my growing up in Israel may have something to do with how I feel connected to the cosmos. I can pick up vibrations that tell me things. I know and feel things other people don't know, like I feel the masculine and feminine poles of situations, I know things before they happen, colors mean things to me. I can read the color of the sky or the color of the ground, and I take these cosmic messages and apply them to me. I'm not deep enough into my consciousness to be able to read all the unknown signals in the universe. This is why I came.

"I want to get so deep into myself that I can pick up the universal signals better. I know they are there. I want to study parapsychology. I applied to the doctoral program at Duke. I would go into Primal Therapy but it's $7000. I wrote Janov three times already but he said I have to wait. I know my pain is so down deep and I'm not sure this therapy can go deep enough. I want to spend my life studying the effects of drugs on my consciousness. I'd say the thing that most interests me are altered states of consciousness . . .

"I have some vibrations off you now. A blue color comes off of you. That's for women, but I feel you have . . . I don't know . . . you have made some trips yourself, not acid, but that this isn't off the wall to you."

Around this time I ask him to tell me how he happened to get his car, as I feel it represents a real interest, an autonomous act meaningful to him. I do not work on his problem with urination since at this moment there is nothing he can do about it. The car seems less compulsive than other actions he has mentioned, and it indicates a direction of moving out on his own.

He recounts with pleasure the story of buying the car and goes into his mother's fear every time he leaves the house, feeding him with tales of danger and death on the road. Both his parents objected to his buying the car; he loves driving but has to go very slowly, afraid that he will "get bumped off" if he speeds. After sharing with me the story of buying the car, he appears more relaxed and spontaneously recalls his earliest memory: "I know this is linked to my problem of urinating. When I was 3 or 4, I remember my mother asking me to urinate. I said no. I remember her looking sad or disappointed, and then I said yes. My problem has something to do with my mother being depressed. Maybe I caused it.

"Here's a story about my mother. In my second year at college, I made the psychology honor society 'cause I had all A's, and so the local Bronx paper somehow found out and there was this article saying 'JOE X MAKES LEHMAN COLLEGE PSYCHOLOGY HONOR SOCIETY.' So I showed it to my mother and she read it and she said, 'So? What has that got to do with me?' I said, 'Ma, read it again,' and she did and again, 'So?' I said, 'Ma, look at the name. Joe X. That's me.' She looked and said, 'That's funny. I didn't recognize your name till you showed it to me.' And that was her comment."

I ask him what he made of that and he says, "My mother doesn't know there's a world outside this door and she doesn't want me to find it, I guess." I state that that makes sense to me and that our time is up. "Just one more thing," he says. "I have to tell you that I have a feeling, more than a feeling, a convinction, that I can be a famous person. I know that I can be a great psychologist and make a contribution to mankind." I smile and tell him I'll see him next week.

To enable Joe to get more acquainted with himself, I focused on the inner realities of his experience and interpreted his struggles, articulated the subtle nuances of change when I saw them. I reflected on where I thought he had come from in a particular situation ("You never spoke up to your girlfriend before"), and where he was moving ("You were able to assert yourself"). Thus I pointed out and explored changes or movement that he presented about himself and others, different experiences of time, different sensations of any kind. I asked questions to increase his capacity to differentiate between experiences: "Was there anything different being with Jane today?" In this way I alerted Joe to a new way of thinking about his experience and this suggested that change was possible. I asked him to clarify what wasn't clear to me. I told him at times how I saw him working or struggling in a particular direction so that I represented with coherent symbols what felt to him like confusion. For example I once told him, "You have been submissive and are trying to find another way to be with Jane." Throughout our contact I stressed that when people *move* out of being like their parents, it is anxiety-provoking.

After four sessions Joe tells me delightedly that his mother only has to be one room away instead of two for him to urinate. He wonders if she hears the noise, feeling ashamed to think she can.

He and Jane attend a rock concert with thousands of other people. There he got stoned, got undressed all day, and urinated in front of everyone, convinced he was Christ. After this concert, he had his first fight with Jane after dating her for a year. He made contact with his own fury with her.

I point out that he was not only able to face this but also he was able to express deep feelings for her for the first time. I am careful not to label them angry feelings, since his image of himself as Christ does not allow him to tolerate anger; his self-effacement and "cool" facade forbid the word "fury" to pertain to him. I tell him that I sense that his feelings are genuine. I also point out in this session that the upstate New York rock festival is geographically the furthest he has ever been from his parents. He then speaks of his anger towards Jane and his mother, who didn't want him to go, and his feeling that he can help mankind.

Upon my return from vacation, much time in sessions is spent describing what a bitch Jane is. He can see her controlling him, how he has always subjected himself to her; he is fed up.

He then has his first homosexual experience, which occurred with his friend David. He says he is glad to be bisexual; he likes "not the sex part but knowing somebody well and sleeping with them and still being friends." He describes the pleasure of the "skin contact" with David and recalls sleeping with his mother for four weeks at age 13 in the Catskill Mountains, saying, "I have been looking for that feeling of being next to my mother ever since."

Instead of discussing homosexuality as pathology, we explore how after sleeping with David he feels good about moving close to a person, feeling freer.

In September and October, what I try to do is to enable Joe to appreciate that the struggles and changes he is facing with Jane are the result of his having begun to seek experience beyond the confines of his compulsive behavior in the past. I emphasize that it is new for him to assert himself with a woman, with anyone, and new experiences confront us with anxiety and self-doubt. I state that it is a change to be in a first give-and-take relationship with a women where he wasn't submissive all the time. In effect, I represent the inner chaos, ups and downs, panics, with a word, "change." I contrast his not submitting all the time with Jane with what went on in his family. I encourage him to stay with this anxiety by asking him to tell me what he was experiencing in this relationship with Jane. While talking he would at times experience the feelings he has with Jane so that talking becomes a living action itself. As this happens, I note less inappropriate smiling and my own increased relaxation with him. After a fist fight with Jane, Joe's anxiety and fury reach the level of intolerance and he breaks off their relationship for a time.

Immediately after this, in November, Joe reports feeling depressed and lonely. He has many fears and phobias: he is afraid to go into a restaurant as everyone laughs at him; he can't undress in front of men as his penis is too small; foods are sprayed with poisonous preservatives so he can't eat them; he can get killed easily in his car on the parkways; he is afraid to speak out in class.

He then reminds me that although he hasn't mentioned his symptom for a while, he still has it and is back to urinating only when anybody is two rooms away. I have an intuition that although he is lonely and sad, angry, being alone without Jane has given him some movement towards greater connection to himself. I ask him, "What is going on with you in your room when you're alone?" I sense pre-rationally that something good is happening with him in his room.

He mentions the predictable fantasies of self-hate, masturbation, being bored, feeling afraid that he has no interests, feeling that he should go out to meet other women but is afraid to. As he talks, I say, "What else? Anything else?" I pursue my hunch. Finally he blushes and laughs and says, "Well, I'm dancing if that's what you mean." I ask what is happening and he describes his life-long inhibition about dancing. He wanted to but couldn't, so he is practicing in his bedroom with rock music. Many associations to feeling that his body is awkward emerge, comparing himself to his father, whom he experiences as much bigger than himself.

He also tells me he can do only one thing well, and that is to play basketball. But he hasn't played since high school. After telling me this, he begins to play basketball on Sundays.

I stay with his experience while dancing. He begins to get into the dancing, "to feel looser," reports liking it but not believing he can do it in front of others. Then one night while he is dancing, his father bursts through his bedroom door. His father screams to his mother: "Hannah, the nut is dancing. Come see."

At this point I am very active. I articulate the strength of his behavior rather than allow him to fall into his habitual self-hate. I say, "It means something to you. You are finding more of your own personal sense of who you are."

In December he tells his father to "get another flunkey to write your letters," continues to dance, and his mother develops migraine headaches. I state that when his image of the good, sweet, scholarly boy shifted to that of a lively, dancing person, everyone in his household became anxious. In December his self-derogating criticism abates somewhat. He talks of his mother's not wanting him to have fun and of her inability to live. I say, "I believe you see self-destruction in your mother and are beginning to object to self-destruction when you see it in other people and in yourself."

He begins to identify more differences between himself and his parents. In December he stops taking drugs. He has not tripped on acid since October, and has cut out all grass, saying that he cannot concentrate in school.

In January he begins to study yoga breathing techniques on his own but complains bitterly of my lack of help. He asks how can he get another girlfriend while saying "I like you, but could you go two rooms away so I can pee?" I inquire about the yoga rather than about his dissatisfaction with Jane. He says he wants to learn to breathe because he is a "shallow breather." He describes feeling "freezing" ever since emigrating from Israel. I point out that he wears only a light-weight flannel jacket in January. I ask about his not wearing a winter coat. What emerges is a hatred for his one winter coat, the image of "manliness" he likes from wearing only a jacket, and feeling intimated while shopping since he feels he has to buy something if a salesman approaches him. I state, "I hear you trying to warm yourself, to comfort yourself. But also you are currently at the mercy of every waiter and coat salesman in New

York. We can discuss your feeling vulnerable to total strangers."

Later in January he is angry with me, insisting that I am forcing him to buy a coat. He experiences my asking why he doesn't wear a coat as undermining his little bit of autonomy. He threatens to leave treatment. I do not deal with his "being forced to" but instead deal with what I see as forward movement. I state that he is beginning to feel into his organic processes and can sense his shallow breathing. He is facing his own inner coldness, which means he is making some contact with himself, and now he wants to bolt.

In January and February he feels much worse. He says he is very bored, feels no interest in schoolwork. I note to myself that his symptom is enabling him to get closer to himself and what he sees is painful, as it is his inner emptiness. I emphasize in the sessions his "easy high" from pot for four years, his two years of acid, and I say that now he has no more instant escapes. I say this is a painful transition. I say that his pattern has been to look for instant relief with drugs and that now he is changing and beginning to find out where he really is inside. I tell him this takes courage.

He then remembers a time that week when he spoke out spontaneously in class, something he could never do before. Before he would only speak when called upon. He complains more bitterly about being bored with himself and bored with others. I ask, "What do you feel you are involved with now?" He says genuinely, "I want to find out about myself, but this is so slow." I emphasize his exploring his breathing, his thoughts, his dreams, his body, becoming more familiar with himself.

He begins to include in his reports some events from Sunday basketball games. He believes he is a "natural," lamenting his wasted four years of not playing. Towards the end of January he has three dreams, each dealing with being at war, with him and his family on one side and a group of enemies on the other. "My family is at war with the world" is his association to his first dream.

In the January sessions he begins to curse, to show more of a sense of humor, to laugh less frequently, to move more fluidly.

In January and February the complaints about the symptom increase. He isn't sure he will go to grad school, but he will definitely leave home. For the first time in his school life he leaves himself two free days in his last semester to work in a mental hospital to make money in order to leave home. He states he wants help with the urinating problem right away.

I ask about his fear of making noise in his classes, his fear of making noise in second grade, of making noise with his mother at 3 or 4 by saying "no." I suggest he might be afraid of standing out as a separate person in areas other than urinating. He feels this is true and associates it with being afraid to stand out anywhere except when stoned on acid.

Joe continues to complain bitterly, asking me how he can "make" himself pee in front of others. I stress how he has been distant from his body for so long, as evidenced in his shallow breathing, his seeing that his penis is average size but feeling distant from that fact, his difficulty with dancing, his problems with sex.

I mention urinating as an ordinary bodily process and ask how he feels about the words "ordinary bodily process." A flood of furious associations follow the word "ordinary." I say, "You have trouble being involved with ordinary human processes." He says, "That's interesting" and begins a discussion of his superhuman connections to the cosmos, which meant I couldn't understand him. I couldn't pick up the messages he could. He analyzes all of my movements that hour, convinced that I know nothing about sex or drugs or men or women. I say, "What do you feel about being an ordinary human being who pees?" He erupts in a barrage of contempt for me, for people at home, at school, on jobs. He is furious. At the end of the session he says, "What is your message to me?" I reply, "You are another human being who pees."

I felt he was experiencing more of his own being in this session, having experienced his fury and confusion over being a natural, ordinary person. I believed it was necessary for him to experience more of himself before he could bear the anxiety of separating at all from his mother. His increased inner strength was seen predominantly in his being strong enough to bear the disillusioning experience of living his life without drugs. It was also seen in his knowing in his guts that he would have to leave home after college. He said the words "I have to leave home," and I sensed he meant them.

I saw him making more noise than ever at home, by dancing, asking his father for money for a coat, looking for a job, telling his parents he was moving out and might not go to grad school.

In the next session at the end of February, he comes in telling me he had had his first "long talk" with his mother. She told him of her headaches, her unhappiness, her feeling that her life was over. He states he feels guilty, and I say that he can now, having taken a look at himself, look at his mother. He doesn't have to avoid seeing how she is. I ask what he sees, and he says that he sees a miserable, furious woman. He told her she needed therapy.

Then he says, "Why do I recommend something to her that hasn't helped me? I am still the same. My symptom is worse. Now I don't even pee when my parents are in the house." I say, "You have moved from buying a car, to being with Jane, with David, to giving up drugs, to talking in class, to dancing, to yoga, to knowing you want to leave home, to getting interested in yourself, and now you say the symptom is worse. I expected that to happen." He asks, "Why did you?" I say: "There's enough of you present now to know that you're afraid of separating from your family. The most complicated thing for you is to separate from your mother. Urinating is equated with separating yourself as a unique, separate person. Now you are strong enough to begin to engage in that struggle."

Pt: You expected it to get worse because I'm better enough to see that independence scares me.
Th: Now that you're getting better, the struggle for independence is on and when that happens, the symptom always gets worse, since it protected you from facing that struggle.
Pt: I think the hardest thing is to leave my mother behind. She has no life, but I have to leave. I feel so bad for her.

The rest of the session is spent in his fantasies of where he might live when he moves out, what he might do, and how afraid he is. He states that he can see that he's been afraid to leave home really for four years in small ways.

In the following session, Joe comes in and says: "I remember two things you said last time: 'the struggle for independence is on, and the symptom keeps you from facing that struggle.' But more when you said, 'Urinating is equated with separating yourself as a separate person.' I can't quite grasp it, but something happened. I went to David's house and I told him to stand outside the bathroom door, and I peed, and then I asked him if he heard me. After he said 'yes,' I said, 'Let's drop it.' "

Joe looks at me and says, "I know it's a big thing, but I don't want to talk more about it." I say, "Okay." He then goes on to discuss his having found a new job as an aide in a mental hospital.

The work we do as therapists always underlines the holistic process of life's constant changes. When we work to provoke or evoke emotional experiencing, pointing out in the here and now how the patient lives with us in the session, interpreting what the patient is or has struggled with, clearing up ambiguity, pointing out patterns of behavior that enhance or obstruct life, pointing out defenses, working at the growing edge, looking at the forms anxiety takes in the session, clarifying the actuality, providing an environment where facades can be dropped, inquiring, interpreting the roots or sources of the suffering, emphasizing the solutions lived right there in the treatment, going into the experience of the patient — all of these ways of working open up the patient's awareness of his inner movement and show him how life is changing and is being created by him moment by moment.

In facilitating awareness of movement there is an inner transformation in the patient from reacting to life to a sense of creating it as one feels movement and change can and do happen.

Bibliography

1. D. W. Winnicott, 'The Use of an Object and relating through Identifications,' *Playing and Reality*; (New York: Basic Books, Inc., 1971).
2. *Op. cit.*, p. 91.

III. Facilitating Connections to Oneself: Reducing Alienation

To be connected to oneself is to be aware and to experience one's thoughts and feelings, to be aware and experience a fuller spectrum of one's inner life and the life around one. The person then feels he and his action and his life are sufficient. By being interested in his inner life, he then becomes aware of the connection between his efforts and their consequences. He is thus connected to the inevitable fact of total responsibility for his actions.

Patients are cut off from experiencing their thoughts and feelings, from connection to themselves and others. As a result, the patient does not know much of what takes place inwardly or outwardly. What takes place is often minimally or not at all experienced and is not integrated or assimilated as his own. There is often a lot of activity accompanied by feelings of emptiness and meaninglessness. There is a discrepancy between what is done and what is felt. The disparity between what one does and what one wants to do causes great tension.

Karen Horney describes this alienation from the felt sense of self[1]:

The general capacity for conscious experience is impaired. There are for instance many neurotics who live as if they were in a fog. Nothing is clear to them. Not only their own thoughts and feelings but also other people, and the implications of a situation are hazy. . . . Also related, in still less drastic terms, are conditions in which the dimming out is restricted to intrapsychic processes. I am thinking of people who can be rather astute observers of others, . . . yet experiences of all kinds (in relation to other, nature, etc.) do not penetrate to their feelings and their inner experiences, do not penetrate to awareness. At the core of this alienation from the actual self is a phenomenon. . . . It is the remoteness of the neurotic from his own feelings, wishes, beliefs and energies. It is the loss of the feeling of being an active determining force in his own life. It is the loss of *feeling himself as an organic whole. These in turn indicate an alienation from that most alive center of ourselves which I have suggested calling the real self.* (my italics)

The question is then how we enable patients to experience what it is they are living in and going through, what they perceive outside themselves. How do we enable patients to be more connected to their inner processes?

1.1 Working in the present

In psychotherapy we find ways to bring the patient into the present moment so that he can get feedback from others, and so that he can be more connected to what is taking place instead of living in illusory notions of how he thinks the world should be, or on the basis of his assumptions about the world, mechanically lived since childhood.

In participating together in the Present, the patient gains energy from interaction with the therapist. Another way of understanding this is that the health of the therapist activates the healing mechanism in the patient.

Therapy sustains a built-in illusion that present action leads to future results. If you talk now you will improve later, etc. However, the actual point is to see what is going on now. In therapy it is possible only to see what *here is.* I cannot change unless I can see what here is and how I live and exist in the here and now. For this reason the therapist works to bring the patient into the here and now in the session. The patient wants to live in peace, but here, right now, there is chaos. The patient does not connect with this because he doesn't want to get to know this. He wants to be a different way. The patient must be able to see chaos before he can change it. *You can only change something when you know what it is . . . when you are connected with it experientially and once you see how you live it and how you create it.*

Therapy is a process that helps us recognize the nature of our psychological illness. People often see their struggles as coming from the outside, their problems are not felt from within. The work of the holistic therapist is to inspire the patient to get interested in *himself,* not in what is being done to him. As people are encouraged to inquire into the actuality of an event, they come more and more to see their part in this event . . . how they cannot be separated from the event but are creating the event. Thus they are more connected to it as it is taking place from within them.

Although at first people are convinced they have difficulties, as people look at themselves they are surprised to *feel* that they really do have difficulties. People are often so distracted and busy and going after things that they don't know what they are saying in any depth. Often they don't know what the difficulty is. People can describe their problems brilliantly but not experience them. Until they realize them in experience, and are inwardly connected with them, there can be no change. At times people say with wonder, "I really am suffering," as though it just occurred to them although they had talked about suffering for a long time. This inner realization, this opening to what is and being it, not commenting on it, is the process of healing, of connecting to inner events in therapy.

Patients are usually focused on doing, not being. This disconnection from their thoughts and feelings makes putting therapy into practice in daily life impossible or unimportant for many patients.

1.2 Decreasing Dissociation

In *From Instinct to Identity*, Louis Breger[2] discusses how dissociation occurs where there is intense interpersonal anxiety at an early age, so painful that the person cannot let in the full experience of it. "Dissociation involves a splitting off of conflict-producing or anxiety-arousing thoughts, impulses, or actions from one's self-conception" (194). An important treatment question then becomes how to enable patients to connect with their own inner experience so that they are more aware of it as it is taking place.

We see dissociation operating in the physical, cognitive, perceptual, imaginal, affectual, and spiritual dimensions. In the cognitive area the person cannot concentrate, cannot think in terms of goals, does not alter goals on the basis of what he can and cannot do. He does not learn from his life since he often does not experience life as coming from inside him, under his control. Physically the patient does not experience his bodily sensations because he does not hear the signals coming from his body. Perceptually the patient sees the world and himself on the basis of his conditioning; he sees things according to a script telling him how he should be and how life should go — he does not know how to drop this script, and if his script is not followed, he becomes upset. Spiritually the person is unaware of levels of Mind connecting him with all other creatures and with nature. He is preoccupied only with his own ego concerns. Affectually we see that patients are not aware of the intensity of many feelings or how feelings affect their lives. Certain feelings are disconnected from as soon as they arise. When a person's life has been focused on living the way others want him to and protecting himself by escaping from what is going on and preparing for a better future, we see that he finds no value in checking with himself and looking carefully to get to know what he is going through right now.

People do not know how to simply be what they are, without liking or disliking it, comparing it, commenting on it. People do not want to look at and find out what and how their mind is, even though all of life reflects the way the mind thinks and perceives. Patients realize they are struggling with themselves but do not take much interest in contemplating on that process. Questioning in therapy arouses intelligence and pain because the wakefulness forces the development of an appreciation of the world and oneself, as they are.

Instead of looking, reflecting, listening in silence, patients judge what is happening against some idea or image of how things are supposed to be rather quickly. Many patients are not interested in seeing how things are, but in how they want them to be. This is a conditioned response based on an intensely held idea from the past that we are supposed to be different from the way we are. We are afraid to face who we are in fact for fear that it will not be enough, but more deeply, for fear of finding out how we *are* enough and feeling the responsibility that comes from that awareness. It is our compassion for our own suffering, our connection with our own inner aliveness, which creates the anxiety of knowing we must change the way we live or we will be wasting our life.

Because of the patient's fear in looking at himself, the therapist must first *be* the environment in which the patient feels that it is safe to begin to look at what is going on inside of himself from his own perspective. It takes time to discover that he has thoughts and feelings of his own different from those of his parents. Facilitating the patient's opening to feeling while in the session decreases dissociation to where the patient begins to live with involvement in the Present Moment while with the therapist. This involvement in wholehearted participation can take the form of talking, silence, relaxation, hating, sorrow, etc. No matter what the form, healing occurs as long as there is engagement so that the person is experiencing what is taking place, or loses the sense of self-conscious separation and simply is, being who he is right now, what is happening right now.

In the early phases of therapy, the patient resorts to old ways of avoiding the awareness of being in relationship with another person now. This awareness of being with another puts the patient in touch with his own being and he cannot tolerate this contact. Patients have learned ways to erase the existence of others as well as many of their own experiences. Without protection or avoidance, the patient may not be able to bear his inner experience for more than seconds.

1.3 Meeting the patient's need by dropping notions and observing as a way of facilitating connecting to oneself

Our aim is to enable the patient to move into the treatment so that he can begin to connect with himself, to be comfortable enough to drop his facades eventually. It is my clinical experience that the only way to facilitate certain patients' connecting with themselves is to let them be and to respect their need to express who they are at times in unusual or unexpected ways.

At the beginning of the therapy we ask the question "What does this patient need in order to be comfortable enough to drop his facades?" Some patient need a firm, structured approach as psychotherapy begins. Some patients need more freedom so that we set limits with the order that comes from within us. Some benefit from interpretations and others from discussion, what Masterson calls "communication matching."[3] With some patients we cannot intervene much in the "acting in" behavior in the session or they will feel imposed on or frightened or furious and leave treatment. We let these patients be, giving them the space needed to express themselves, finding out who they are, letting them begin therapy in their own way, at their own pace, not ours.

Suggesting the end of acting out patterns and talking instead is helpful, but at times it is more beneficial to be open, to be patient, to learn who the patient is and not try to effect a format except by being open and respectful of fellow human beings. I have at times stood firmly against the patient and insisted that certain forms of therapy be kept. This is when I intuit or see that the patient can benefit from keeping them. By being open to the wide variety of forms that awareness takes, by seeing this is who the patient is right now without evaluation but with participation in a friendly, open, respectful, inwardly calm spirit, the acting out most often drops away. This requires the therapist to be able to respect and not be upset by a wide variety of forms of human protection. I always indicate at some early point my interest in the way the patient is living with me in the session and interest in what it might express. I inquire into his wish to look at what he is confronting with his behavior. If he does not wish to look at this now, I can either drop it or continue, depending on the dosage of anxiety I assess to be useful to the patient now.

It is our "openness mind," as Tarthang Tulku calls it,[4] our being able to drop concepts of how therapy should go, that enables us to have intuitive experiences without conceptions to guide us in the work with some difficult patients who require parameters of treatment. When we clear our minds in the session of concepts of how to work, we can have the clear perception that will integrate our observations into right actions. In this way we work with what Shunryu Suzuki calls "beginner's mind,"[5] realizing we have to be taught what each person needs.

1.3.1 Example of facilitating connection through dropping notions and observing what the patient needs

I answered the phone. A voice with a rough New York accent said, "Are you the therapist?" I said I was and he said, "How do I get to your house? I'm at City College . . . Jane Olsen told me to call you." The voice had the ring of a prize fighter's. After asking how he was coming, I gave directions for the trip by subway. "How 'bout if I come tomorrow?" I told him when I could see him, and he said, "See ya." There was a click, no goodbye.

Later that night he called to say that he had lost the directions. There was no apology. I gave them again. He said, "I may not make it. It depends on if I decide it's worth it. Thanks."

The next day I waited for 40 minutes. It was an evening in early spring. The front door bell rang. I had stated on the phone that the front door would be open and not to ring the bell. I went to the door and through the glass saw a young man dressed completely in black. His face was pale and snide-looking.

He entered the hallway and I introduced myself. He said, "I'm Phil. Where do you operate?" He laughed. I let him to the office and when we entered he said, "You're dressed in orange. Are you one of those Indian spirituals?" His whole demeanor was that of someone who had taken over the office, who had entered illegally but was in charge. He wore old black cotton Army pants, a black turtleneck shirt, a black jacket, a black hat with a wide brim, and black shoes with no socks.

As I looked at him I began to sit. He said, "I'm in mourning. That's why I wear all black. I only wear black these days." I asked him what he mourned and he said that he came to see me because he wasn't sure whether or not he had murdered a man. He was still standing. I did not ask him to sit. He said that he wanted to tell me the story.

He began to talk of how he was driving his car when an old man crossed the highway. The man sank down in front of his car and he slammed on the brakes. It was in the middle of the night and the man was wearing pajamas. He said that he wasn't sure if this was the sequence. Maybe he hit the man and then the man sank. An ambulance came and the doctor said the man had died of a heart attack.

He then sat down and took out a large cigar. He lit it and began to sink back into the chair. I asked him how he was feeling with this not knowing and he said, "The important thing to know is that I have the soul of a murderer. I've threatened to kill so many people that maybe something happened that I did it." He said that he wouldn't kill an old man by choice, but what difference did it really make if somebody whose life was over lived or not — actually?

I heard the buzzer to my office indicating that the next patient had arrived. I had the feeling that Phil did not know that he had come late, that we could only talk for a short time. I told him that we had to stop. He said incredulously, "You're asking me to leave?" I said that he had come late, I had to stop. Laughing he said, "I can't believe it . . . you ask me to leave, and I'm walking around thinking I belong in Matawon." I said that this was it, someone was waiting to see me.

I then told him I would like to see him again and that we could arrange a time now. He said, "No way." I said he owed me X dollars. He laughed and walked over to me, standing close. He said, "You're asking me to pay you X when you saw me ten minutes, and you want it now — right? Well, I have three bucks. Here." He took the three singles and threw them on the floor. I did not respond explicitly to the gesture. I said that I would like to see him again, to call me, and we could arrange another time. I left the money on the floor. He laughed, saying, "I'm leaving my cigar. Maybe you can enjoy it later when all your patients go. Do you kick them all out? . . . Jewish bitch."

Before he walked out the door, I said, "I don't smoke." He turned, looked, smiled and left.

I heard from Phil three weeks later. He said, "I'm coming back . . . I forgot how to get there."

He came on time. As he entered he sang, "Let me entertain you, and we'll have a real good time. And I can. . . . " He walked over to the window where there is a standing lamp, picked it up as if it were a mike, and began to make jokes about my office. He said, "Ladies and gentlemen, I want to tell you how it is to be in therapy with a Park Avenue therapist, not a West Side therapist — somebody who married rich, or is rich. We see an Oriental rug, antique, on the floor. Nothing but the best for the girl who couldn't get into medical school." He did this for about five minutes.

I noticed that he was wearing a pink shirt along with the same black outfit and mentioned this. He said, "I decided the old guy croaked. However, don't get smart or I could do it to you." He then put his finger in his pants to simulate a gun. Before I could get another word out, he said that he wanted me to sit back and "LISTEN . . LISTEN, let your day be a little brighter."

From his back pocket he took out a copy of *Screw* Magazine. He asked me what I would like to hear, mentioning the names of some of the stories. I asked him if he felt this was what he wanted for today. He said, "I'm sure." I asked him what he heard himself saying to me and he said, "I'm a sex maniac. Did you ever work with a sex maniac before?" I asked him what the maniac was involved with and he said, "I will tell you when I'm ready . . . and you will listen or . . . I will not pay you the remainder . . . remember?"

I asked him where he got the money to pay and he said, "I drum . . . and now as I say with my great charm to most ladies, shut up." He spent the hour reading articles and making jokes about them. I did not interrupt him until the end when I said that I wondered how this way of being together was for him. He said, "It sucks. You suck. The world sucks. And I'm making it better for you." I said he was certainly sure of what he wanted. He agreed. I felt a considerable interest to see him again, and felt no need to say anything else.

I then told him that I would like to be paid today for this session and the previous one, and I asked him when he would come again, naming my open time. He said, "Here is the money, sweetie." A crumpled roll of dirty-looking bills was handed to me. He said, "Aren't you going to count it . . . too proud? I could have swindled you . . . I want to see you count it." I asked how come. He said. "I want to see your money-hungry fingers . . . move." I said, "Okay." I counted the money and said thank you. I asked if he wanted to pay by the week or how? He said, "Pay by the week. This is too much." He laughed and did not answer my question. He walked out of the room, laughing, and closed the door behind him.

In the ensuing weeks Phil paraded around the room, putting his hat on in different ways, rearranging his jacket, putting spotlights on himself, telling filthy jokes. Sometimes I laughed and sometimes I didn't, depending on what I heard. Occasionally I would ask what he was confronting in himself with all this show, what he was experiencing today being here, how he was experiencing me, was it different for him now than last week — did he feel he was opening up something new for himself here, or was this compulsive, did his act close off any possibilities as he saw it, in terms of his being here with me.

He answered the questions. He then asked me what I thought he was saying with all this filth on his mind. I said I wasn't sure but that maybe he thought a lot about sex, was confused with something in that area. I said I was a woman and by constantly using pejorative slang for the female anatomy – "slimy cunt," "pussy," "twat," "tit," "jugs" – he was expressing something of how he felt with women – also that it felt okay to express himself here.

He then began to talk a bit of how he wan't comfortable with women. He only took out "freaks" because he was one, girls thought he was nuts, and he was. As for me and my slimy cunt . . . it was just a joke, he said. He thought I was an okay cunt, but he would like it better if I told him some dirty jokes. I said that I didn't work that way. He said, "Oh, you just sit back and don't participate." I said that my work was not to tell jokes, although I could appreciate a good floor show, which he gave. I didn't give them. He asked me if I thought he had given a good floor show and again I said "Yes." He asked me if I thought he was funny, and I said, "Very funny. But you're a lot of other things . . . sometimes you're sentimental, sometimes sad, sometimes mad, sometimes funny."

He then sighed visibly, appeared relieved, and said that he would like to bring his "sticks" to the next session and asked if this would be okay. I said it would, knowing he meant drumsticks.

Then, with utter contempt in his voice, he said, "What kind of therapy is this anyway? You just let me do whatever I want?" I asked him if he felt he had alternatives to this and what they would be. He said, "I want to know what kind of work you do – do I just come in and fuck around?" I said that we were getting to know each other and the way he had chosen to get to know me was occasionally to look at me or ask for my responses during the sessions, that apparently making contact in another way wasn't right for him. I said he needed to do a show and said this probably went on with other people when he felt he didn't know what to expect or wanted something. I said I thought he was showing me something of the way he lived his life, and we could inquire into this if he wanted. He said I was a schmuck and he left.

The following week he sat down on the couch far away from me. It was the first time he began with sitting. He said, "I want to read to you." He spent the next four or five weeks reading from Genet and Ionesco with whom he said he identified. He would read very intently, then look up at me, and ask for my opinion on what was being said.

In this way we got into a discussion of what it would be like to be a criminal, what the mind of the criminal is like, if he is a criminal. He said, "I wonder if I belong in jail. I would like to be there . . . then I would have to decide anything . . . don't talk . . . don't say anything to that. I know how you work, you figure things out . . . right? I'm gonna tell you what it means. It means that I'm already in jail. Don't answer." I kept quiet for a moment and then said, "Are you?" He ignored the question, went back to reading, which led to some intellectual discussions about prostitution, jail, liars, deceit, fakery, and violence. I did not ask him to make it any more personal than it already was. He was involved with being a prostitute in jail, a liar, a fake, and violent in ways I could not yet know. My work was to wait, to listen, to appreciate his unqiue way of moving into our relationship.

Phil told me that he liked to hear the sound of his own voice – he didn't like it when I said anything. He liked it when I listened. He could tell when I was thinking he was reading well. He told me that he was a phony intellectual. He told me he felt awful about his teeth, which were more yellow than white. He hated his small, dark brown eyes. He hated being on the short side. He hated his body because it was puny. He hated his pale complexion.

He then talked about my body in the most intimate terms, telling me what he liked, what he didn't. I asked him if he could get anywhere other than the body with me, with himself, and he said, "No, I'd say I'm strictly a body man." I said that was the place where the child registers his first sensations and a good place to begin. He said, "You're smart and a wise ass. Don't call the shots." I told him he was smart and a wise ass and asked if he saw that. He laughed.

He then began to read from a journal be kept on some of his impressions of people on the street. He kept track of what he had to say each day. The journal was very dirty and had pages inserted and torn out. I asked him what would it be if he didn't write down life. He said that was very nasty. I said that in my experience people who write it down often don't feel they live it. Phil got angry and insulted my need for supremacy over him, my need to castrate him by telling him he wasn't living, my need to be better than he was. He said that I could take my books and shove them since they hadn't taught me to be sensitive.

I was silent for several minutes and saw that he was trembling. I said that I was sorry, that I didn't know he didn't want me to talk about his life. He screamed, "I didn't say that. You made fun of me. You have to say you did." I said that I could see that this had upset him – but I didn't know how come. He got up and said, "Specialist. Specialist. Get wise, and don't give me any prescriptions. Take all your chairs, there are five chairs in here, and . . . forget it." He got up and walked out.

Phil called me four weeks later. He said that he would like to tell me personally that I was a rotten therapist and he had put up a note at the college counselling center to this effect, that they had taken it down, that he had had a fight with the psychologist there about me. That he had personally decided to tell all his friends that worked with the student union that I stank, but that this was all a waste of time. I said, "It's nice to hear from you. Why don't you come in?" He laughed and hung up the phone.

The next time he called I laughed and said that I only had five minutes to be insulted. He said, "I want to come in as a patient this time." There was a less defensive tone, a trace of softness. I said that I could see him today . . . no good . . . tomorrow . . . no good. I asked, "When?" He said seriously, "In three weeks." We made an appointment. I felt glad that he was coming.

Phil came in and sat down on the chair. He said he wanted to talk about his plans for his future, that he had gotten fired from a decent weekend job drumming. The same thing – a fight. There was a fist fight this time, he was glad it had happened, but he wasn't sure he could make a living working as a full-time drummer. He was graduating from college after summer session. He had no real plans. He wanted to get his own place but he had spent all his money, he had to live with his parents.

He talked non-stop, asking few questions, describing his situation. He said, "I feel really bum. Not about the job . . . about how I can't do anything. I want to write, to play music, but I can't do anything." He sat quietly.

I asked, "What do you want in life?" He seemed startled by the question and said, "I never asked myself that question really . . . I mean I've asked it, but . . . I don't know. I want everything. I want the works." "You're not sure what you want?" I felt that for the first time we were creating the moment and living in it together. I looked at him with recognition of this fact. There was a deep respect in me for this young man. He had been seeing me off and on for four months. I had let him be. He had begun to trust me a bit in this time.

In this case we see how this patient begins to open up and trust. He moves more into the here and now in his interaction with the therapist at his own tempo in his own way. He opens up with short flashes of being in the moment, connecting with his inner feelings of what is going on and thus lets in a greater range and depth of emotional experiencing. We thus find the patient connecting in actuality more with his inner experiencing, not just talking about it. In this process the patient is finding out more who he is *as is*. The objective of therapy is being actualized in *the mutual discovery* of what is. Here the therapist provides the structure for the patient by being inwardly centered, calm, open, respectful, able to be free enough of concepts to learn how to proceed, trusting the patient's wish to find himself and trusting that human goodness is a fact that will be revealed. These attitudes and values are empathically conveyed to the patient when they exist.

At these moments of deeper participation in the moment, there is a transformation of both patient and therapist. The participants shift their commitment from escaping tension to being in the moment. The patient learns to return to direct and simple experience. No matter what it is, the experience can then become sufficient in itself. Connecting directly to the emotions as they are emerging awakens the healing powers available in human relating.

Such moments of being involved in experiencing, being aware of being together, extend themselves as the work goes on. *It is in the experiencing of the here and now as sufficient, it is in the participation in the moment, the involvement in the Present, that connection to oneself is faciliated and alienation is reduced.*

1.3.2 Clinical example of working in the here and now and facilitating connections to oneself

In this session you will see the therapist focus on what is taking place in the here and now in the patient, in the therapeutic interaction.

A patient has been in treatment once a week for 3 months. He missed his last session. He has not paid me for the last 3 weeks. He promised to mail me a check last week but has not done this.

This 35-year-old, attractive, divorced man is a self-employed industrial consultant. He lives with his sister and his sister's girlfriend who is also his "sometime lover." He is currently involved with many women, many philanthropic organizations, with sports, with social clubs, and with making a success of his own business. He came to treatment unclear as to what was bothering him, "not sure that anything is . . . except that I see my closets as a metaphor of my life perhaps; they are chaotic, filthy, unorganized. I have to have a housekeeper in when I have a dinner party just to do the closets . . . and I have a lot of closets as I have this big place. I can't keep it all together. It's exciting and yet I wish I could keep my house in order. Do you hear something in that?" He laughs in a charming way. This man comes from a wealthy family, has been successful in a few professional projects, was a highly successful athlete, has an advanced degree in socio-biology and wants to turn "corporate animals into compassionate creatures." It is particularly important to him that everyone know that his father is a multi-millionaire; he cherishes the "power it gives me over almost everyone I meet." He said, "In some circles just my name alone sends girls into a faint. I love it."

He begins the session with how he had called me when he missed his last session, giving reasons for missing it and saying that he had forgotten to send the money. He says he will send me the money today. Then he smiles slightly. I ask, "What are you saying with your smile?" He almost laughs, saying, "Well, I probably won't do it." I ask quietly, "How come?" He says that he may not remember. Maybe he will see something in a store that he wants to buy; that he can't keep track of things he has so many projects going on right now; but that he will definitely send it to me if he can keep it in mind. Again there is a smile, not as broad. I say that his smiling suggests that he might be enjoying something going on here. What could it be? He says that he is thinking that I probably have more money than he does so that "I don't really care, to be honest . . . I mean if you get it this week or in a few weeks . . . what's the big deal? I don't think it's any big deal . . . it's not like I'm way overdue paying."

He then talks about how overdue he is in several restaurants in the city, that he wines and dines important people there and that he always pays eventually. He says, "It's part of being rich that you don't pay your bills on time." He smiles and says that he does care but that with paying me he can talk a good game of caring but that it's mostly bullshit. I say that it is not bullshit to me, asking for money, needing money to live. He agrees, and then talks of how much he cares for all the starving people since he gives to some African fund, but that "if a truckload of starving kids fell out in front of me on my way to buying some wine, I wouldn't look back once."

He says that he does care about his cat, his girlfriend, his snake. I observe that as he talks here he is in fact more caring. He then talks about feeding rats to his snake and all the people who consider him cruel, but they eat meat, etc. There is some talk of hypocrisy in various friends, but not in him. I ignore this diversion and say, "If I say that I want you to pay me, you suggest it will be similar to seeing a truckload of starving people on your way to the wine store?" He says, "If you did say that you wanted me to pay, I would." He shrugs his shoulder . . . I repeat the gesture. He says, "Well, frankly, I would chalk it off to your not caring about me, or that money was more important than me." I say, "I do want to be paid for September." He looks at me and does not smile. He says he will send it today. Again he does not smile. He then tells me how he can't keep track of all the exciting things going on at work, and he discusses some new ideas for business projects.

While talking he is looking down at his new ornate cowboy boots. I say, "Are your boots new?" He says that they are; he got them when he bought new shoes. "Everything is so expensive now. I can't keep up. A pair of shoes costs eighty dollars, a good pair of shoes." *There was a slightly softer edge of feeling in his voice as he says "a good pair of shoes."*

I say, "You know your voice changed as you were telling me that a pair of shoes costs eighty dollars, as you said 'a good pair of shoes.' What are you feeling now?" He says that he feels embarrassed, kind of ashamed that he spends so much on his clothes. "I don't know why." I ask, "What is there that embarrasses you with telling me that you spend eighty dollars for shoes, a good pair?" He says, "I know that it shows that I have to keep up this rich front, that I have to prove that I'm rich. It's phony of me." I say, "We were just talking of your not paying me and you went into telling me how much money you were spending on clothes." He says, almost laughing, "Right. I am more important than you. I am, for sure. I know I don't care if you don't get the money, I mean I figure you have lots of other clients so if I don't pay, so what?" He goes into talking of how he gives money away to charity and this sort of absolves him from not caring.

I say, "How do you imagine I feel when I tell you I depend on my income to live, you haven't paid me, then you talk of how vastly you're spending on clothes?" He says instantly with a charming grin, "I suppose you don't like me but, frankly, I feel bitter . . . I feel fucked and . . . for some reason I just thought of my wife and how she left me, and she didn't care enough to want to work on the marriage." He then talks of his bitterness and hurt about his ex-wife. He stops, and I ask him to tell me more of his bitterness, and he talks of how he was about 6 or so when his parents were divorced. They didn't tell him about it before. It was all handled very well, "very sweetly, but nobody talked to me about how it was for me. My sister went to a shrink. I thought it stank of them not to share it before, and I figured how much could they care?" I say, "You felt your parents didn't care for you then?" He says with feeling, "Why do you think I'm into all this work on tribal killing, and tribal structure, and I spend all my time trying to get these monster organizations to break down and get together . . . you know my whole life's work is pretending in these workshops that I have compassion . . . when I don't have it, and I don't feel it. I don't know what it is." After a pause I say, "Yes."

He then begins to talk about his ability to con everyone. I say that I don't believe he can do this, as it is sometimes possible to see when he is not sincere and when he is sincere. He can see this is true for people who look, but "who looks?" He tells me how he hates to be conned and asks if he told me the story of the guy across the hall who conned him during the summer. I don't answer and he goes on saying, "I can't remember if I told you . . . so much grass goes to the brain . . . anyway." Then he tells me how this young man promised to build him a loft bed when he was on vacation, did a good job of conning him into believing he could do it; when he returned the bed was done poorly and not finished. He then said, "He conned me into believing he could do it. I had an emotional reaction to the guy." Here he smiles in a completely different way. It was a clean, happy smile unlike the others, which were seductive or sadistic or nasty. I mention this to the patient by saying, "You really had an emotional reaction to that guy." He says, "Yeah, it was great. To have an emotion . . . maybe that's it. I think it is. I mean I hardly ever feel . . . you know, I realize something . . . I hardly ever let love in. I can feel it all across my chest, the barrier, keeping myself back. You know, when I make love to a woman, I can make love but I can't feel the love coming from the woman . . . I can't let them in." He then says with feeling, "I am very bitter." I say, "I can see that." There is a moment of silence, and I say, "You let some feeling in today." He says, "I got it." He points to his mid-chest.

I say our time is up. He stands up saying he would send me a check. He says that he intends to pay for the session he missed last week. He says, "See you." He does not thank me for the session as he had in all the previous sessions, for three months. I notice that he does not close the door to the office behind him as he had done before, but leaves it open a bit.

By focusing on what is going on in *the here and now* in the sessions (here, the new kind of smile), what is genuine, and what is observably taking place in the interaction, the therapist sees the session as a time when ways of living are being changed as we go along.

D. W. Winnicott speaks of the therapist as the "facilitating environment."[6] Heinz Kohut speaks of the empathic "mirroring" of the therapist.[7] Masud Khan speaks of the therapist as "the protective shield."[8] All of these phrases relate to the question of how we can be and do what the patient needs in order for him to use the work of psychotherapy. In order to meet the needs of the patient we must be able to experience inwardly what this unique patient needs and then to act on this. One might say when we let go of concepts we experience how it is for the patient. For moments we are alone with the patient. We are *being with the experience of the patient* and then we are clear as to what action to take in the therapy.

1.4 Using imagery to facilitate connections to oneself

Much has been written indicating that in sessions some patients are all over the place, move from one topic to another, often forgetting what they said, are not sure what they are doing in treatment, feel little more over time, spend much time in treatment confused as to what they are working on and cannot put the insights they gain into practice in daily life. At times I use imagery to enable such patients to connect with their inner life.

Using imagery takes the patient right into the experience. It guides him to his senses and to finding from within some way of focusing on some potential solutions to the often confusing picture he otherwise discusses. Imagery enables the patient to work from within, thus to feel there is *more inside*. It also offers a way for the patient to look at new possibilities where he has previously seen none. It allows him to feel that he can do something about his situation. The work with imagery takes the patient out of his sometimes obsessive, sometimes endless, sometimes confused and affectless talk. It almost always takes the patient out of his self-conscious, dualistic participation in therapy where one person has the answers and the other doesn't, where one person is the object to be done to and the other is the one who can fix things. There are some patients with whom the standard therapeutic methods have failed to move the patient into ever wanting to struggle with or reverse their most comfortable, habitual tendencies which severely limit their freedom to live openly in life.

I have used imagery with patients who are narcissistic and borderline and are very disconnected from feelings, with neurotic patients who are anxious and alientated, to help them relax and experience feelings, with patients who are inwardly so disorganized or confused that they are not clear what they are working on, with patients who have obsessive ruminating to move them to the experiencing realm, and with patients who have been in therapy a lot before but who do not feel much or where there is difficulty moving the insights into daily life.

As I have written elsewhere:

> In the work with imagery [the patient] learns what it is to be engaged rather than distanced from what is happening. He has a touchstone for how deep, exciting and good and varied life can be. In working with the imagery he is creating the moment, he is creating what takes place. He is not doing what someone else has told him to do, he is freed from the pressures of his mother's or father's image of who he is. He can be who he is. He develops more ability to look within rather than habitually to lay blame outside himself. ... The patient becomes more whole, less fragmented, as there is more of him participating in the moment. The exercise allows the patient to reverse habitual ways of seeing himself and living with others. The focus of the work is not on what the matter is, but on what is actually taking place. ... The flow of being in the moment, open to what happens, shows the patient how to be in life without having to control what goes on. The work includes one's relationship to oneself, others, the universe, nature, space, and time. Thus the patient is offered an opportunity to move beyond the fragment of his ordinary egocentric preoccupations.[9]

In most of the imagery work I have done, the patient has a deeply affective experience, he feels new and fresh afterwards and is able to experience it deeply and act on what he has found in the imaginal realm. The patient feels very good about the experience, feels the experience as very much being his own, identifies with it and works with it. Regardless of whether the patient is borderline, narcissistic, or neurotic, there is almost always an easy movement into the work. In using imagery patients experience the session as exciting and full of hope. What is particularly striking is the quality of affect produced as contrasted with what usually happens, and the way the patient connects with what they have found in their imagery, or in work with their imagination. Patients see new things about themselves, experience more of themselves, and do not deny this. Patients can at times own the work to where they begin to show new patterns of living in everyday life after the work.

1.4.1 Examples of using imagery to facilitate connections to oneself

Example One: A 30-year-old married narcissistic man was a college math teacher. He wanted to live more openly as a transvestite, but knew he was afraid to do this. He would talk without stopping in the session, bringing in boundless material including dreams that took 20 minutes to report, fantasies of never-ending quantity often having to do with sex, a flooding of data from his daily life where the colors and textures and bodily sensations and impressions and interpretations and analysis and various humorous treatments of events were reported. He would often describe his large collection of wood scraps but he wasn't sure why he had kept them. He spent hours shopping for women's clothes for himself, taking make-up lessons, voice lessons, going to bars, ruminating about not writing professional papers. The patient was not able to organize any of this experience. He would often intersperse his graphic and literary and poetic assemblage with fragments of songs or symphonies or poems or whistling so that I would know what he meant.

He often talked about being with his mother as a child, walking with her on the street holding her hand, being with her in the apartment. At these times, some feeling would be experienced and then he would run from it into more dreams and fantasies.

He sometimes talked of his father, and sometimes described going up a steep hill on his way to grade school, during which time he would get nauseated and very tense. He did not know what any of these things connected with in his daily life, nor much of their meaning to him. In sessions he wanted to tell me everything . . . his brilliant mind never stopped processing external details. Sometimes dream transcriptions ran over 10 pages. Frequently the patient would say, "This is all too much." The question was how to help him connect with any of this.

After several months, one day when he was talking about his mother, I asked the patient to close his eyes, to remain relaxed and just breathe in an even and regular way. He had been talking about his mother being in their apartment. It was dusk.

Th: Tell me with your eyes closed what it is you see in this room, what you hear, what you feel and what you do.

Pt: (describing the room in detail) . . . I see my mother standing near the easel. She's painting. I see the back of her, and I am standing at the kitchen door by the kitchen.

Th: What do you hear?

Pt: I hear the sound of her brush on the easel . . . I hear like a humming noise . . . it is every quiet . . . (small silence) . . . I hear my own breathing . . . 'cause I want to go to her, but I can't.

Th: And what do you feel?

Pt: I feel very sad. I see her sadness. I feel afraid to see this.

Th: And what do you do?

Pt: I don't do anything. I stand and watch her. I want to go over to her and give her a kiss, but then I would just want to throw my arms around her and cry and talk about my dad, and ask her where he was or I would just want to console her and tell her everything would be all right. She is very tired. I am just standing there 'cause I'm afraid and I don't know what to do.

Th: You see your mother and you are there watching her. What do you wish to do next?

Pt: I go into the kitchen and start to fix something in there. I see that I'm fixing this can opener. I don't want to see her now. I don't want to go back in there so I just stay in the kitchen and get busy with working. She comes in then and seems me fixing and she tells me this is very nice. She tells me to go and set the table and that she is going to fix dinner. I get the tablecloth from this little closet in the hall . . .

Th: Describe the tablecloth to me.

Pt: (silent for a moment) It is white and it has little green and purple flowers on it . . .

Th: And the feel of the cloth?

Pt: Like a rough cotton . . . like a cheap and kind of hard cotton . . .

Th: And how are you feeling?

Pt: I feel lonely . . . and . . . sad. (begins to cry – there are several seconds of crying) I want to give my mom a big hug or have her hold me . . .

Th: So do that . . . go into the kitchen and see how to do that.

Pt: I walk back into the kitchen. My mom is at the sink. She's washing lettuce. I walk up to her and put my arms around her . . . and my head is up against her stomach. (begins to cry)

Th: And what happens next?

Pt: My mother says, "Don't cry, Mikey. I know you miss Daddy, but we'll be okay." She pats my hair and then . . . (crying very hard)

Th: What do you hear?

Pt: I say, "I love you, mama." (patient is crying very hard)

Th: See yourself with your mother in the kitchen standing there walking up to her and putting your arms around her, knowing this is something inside of you . . . and that this feeling is something that you have, that you can come back to . . . and now find yourself back on the couch, open your eyes, knowing you have found something you need inside.

Pt: I hardly ever see my mom now . . . I feel so bad when I see her, she is so sad. But I guess there's something in me that wants to get to know her again . . . (silence). I feel very much how I felt a lot . . . kind of lonely and sad, but right now I feel very good. I guess it's being able to feel. See how I turned away from going into the room? I do that all the time with Eva. It's like I constantly move away from my own feelings. I would like to do this work some more. It gives me right now some idea of why I'm coming and most of the time I can't remember.

Following this work with imagery the patient reported feeling more alert, feeling that he could have relationships with people he cared about. He reported having more energy. He called his mother for the first time in months and met after her work. For five years he had wanted to tell her he was a transvestite. During the course of their meal together, he did tell her for the first time.

Example two: Patient comes in after several weeks insisting that she has nothing inside, that she is nothing, that she has nothing to say. She is very angry. I ask her if she would be willing to do a short exercise with imagery where she would close her eyes for a moment. She agrees.

Th: Imagine yourself standing on a beach. You bend down and pick up three grains of sand. Imagine these three grains in the palm of your hand. Now tell me what they turn into.

Pt: I see one grain turning into a key, a small gold metal key, and the other a flower.

Th: Describe the flower, and tell me how it feels, how many petals it has.

Pt: I see a bright red rose, dark red, now very dark red with a closed up center and some petals around it . . .

Th: How many petals are there?

Pt: I see six petals.

Th: And the feel of the rose?

Pt: The flower feels smooth and soft, and gentle . . . (slight smile . . . a more relaxed breathing) . . . and the stem is all thorny and sticky like needles.

Th: Good. Now the third grain in the palm of your hand. What does it turn into?

Pt: I see a round crystal . . . and the light is reflected in it.

Th: Describe the color of the light in the crystal.

Pt: It's bright yellow like the sun reflected in it . . . I want to put the crystal down on the beach.

Th: So do it. And tell me how you see the crystal on the sand.

Pt: It's sitting there on the beach and to the left I see some blue water, like the beginning of maybe the ocean, and then on the right some beach grass.

Th: Do you want to leave the crystal there?

Pt: I want to put it in the grass so that it won't be all alone.

Th: Good. So do that. And tell me what you see yourself doing.

Pt: Well, I just pick it up and carry it over to the grass.

Th: And do you see anything on the way?

Pt: I see the sand, and just the grass, and there is sunlight.

Th: What do you see yourself doing now?

Pt: I take the crystal and I want to leave it in the grass, but I want to give it some kind of cover so that no one will take it.

Th: So imagine your cover and describe it to me.

Pt: I see a piece of light purple silk, long and thin. It's very soft, and it has sort of a sparkly thing on it.

Th: Describe this sparkly thing.

Pt: It's like little silver threads running through the silk, and it shines.

Th: Take your scarf and cover your crystal that you have now in the beach grass in the sand and tell me what you see happening.

Pt: I just put the scarf over the crystal. No, first I dig in the sand, and bury the crystal, and then I cover it with the scarf. But then I have to put some little rocks over the scarf so the wind doesn't blow it away. Then I just finish and . . .

Th: What happens next?

Pt: Well, I see the key and the rose on the beach now, and I want to put them . . . no, just put the key with the crystal, so I do that. I bury the key, but the rose – I just lay the rose next to the scarf.

Th: And how are you feeling?

Pt: I feel very good, very happy . . . very content.

Th: So then know that you have found your key, and your flower and your crystal, and that you have them in a place where you can return to them when you want to. Know that you have found a way to protect them with the purple scarf, and say goodbye to the beach for now and just take a few breathes. Open your eyes.

The patient says that she wants to feel this kind of feeling in her daily life. She says that she would like to find inside herself the sunny feeling she found on the beach. I say, "It is inside of you. We shall find it again and again. Does this image show you any ways you might find it?" The patient mentions the crystal and how maybe this says something about her interest in jewelry and stones. She says that she has been toying with the idea of taking a jewelry-making class but that she is always considering something or other that she doesn't do. I say that the image opens some possibilities in life. She says that she might do something. Her affect is much more positive. This patient then signed up for a jewelry class at her local YMHA and has maintained her interest in this. We worked with imagery off and on with the patient often finding something inside which gave her a way to find some direction from inside. Prior to this the patient was convinced that she was "a void" inside.

Going into the details of the sensory experience enables the patient to move more into experiencing the image, which is always his own very personal inner statement and is felt differently from the alienated feelings of many other sessions. In using imagery, the patient is calling on right brain functioning rather than working with the intellect. He is working with imagination, where everything is creative and new and not compulsive, as pointed out by Dr. Gerald Epstein in *Waking Dream Therapy*, his book describing imaginal work as a new form of therapy.[10]

1.5 Questions as a way of increasing connection to oneself

The primary purpose of questions is not to gain information from the patient but to facilitate the patient's process of telling so that he has an experience in the telling, so that there is the discovery of the involvement in living/sharing through telling the therapist. By answering questions, the patient's self-consciousness drops away and *he finds how it is to participate with another from within so that he is stronger inwardly. Questions enable the patient to gain a sense of what it is to be creating himself in the moment as he answers, discovering from within.* Questions inspire participation of a wholehearted kind. As patients are inspired to question or look at their inner life, they become more interested in the process of looking and questioning, rather than blaming or doing. It is the process of involved participation and interest in looking that is at the core of therapy. Therapy is a process of clarifying actuality, so that in the participation the patient breaks through his separation from himself and is at one with the telling. The patient loses the self-consciousness that separates man from his being whole and wholly who he is.

It is often in the process of answering questions that the patient finds out who he is. In the process of answering, we discover that we create new and true answers only when we begin with a not-knowing, innocent, fresh mind. It is for this reason that questions are so important in treatment. Shunryu Suzuki says, "So to talk about ourselves is actually to forget about ourselves."[11]

With our questions we can change the level of discourse from the concrete to the abstract, from the abstract to the concrete, from shallow discourse to deeper discourse. With questions we reduce fragmentation and dissociation and enable the patient to get interested in his inner life. With questions we move patients to living in the moment and finding more of who they are.

Many therapists I have supervised have difficulty thinking of questions that will inspire the patients' interest in themselves. The following are some of the questions I've used to direct the patient inwards. As with everything in therapy, these questions must be timed sensitively and directed towards the needs of the patient.

What is your way of living in that situation, with that person?

What was meaningful to you in all that?

What is fearful to you?

What is it that bothers you?

What could end that anger, fear (etc.) for you?

What did your behavior open up for you?

What did your action close down?

Tell me some of the inner ways you experienced that situation, event, encounter, relationship, etc.

What do you hear yourself saying now?

What do you see yourself doing in that situation to get what you want? to keep from getting what you want?

Are there other options in living in what you describe?

What are some other possibilities for seeing this whole thing?

Does what you did feel natural to you? Tell me how.

Does what you did feel unnatural to you? Tell me how.

Do you think this reveals your true nature? In what way?

What in this was who you are? What was your mother, father, sister, brother, lover, teacher, wife, husband, etc.?

What image do you try to project in this? How do you want people to see you?

What is the whole big thing you are living in, how would you put the whole thing?

What do you know, feel, think that you aren't saying so far?

What is it you see yourself struggling with in what you are saying?

Were you using your capacities, talent, intelligence in this thing — where do you see this?

Where in this did you hit your habitual pattern? What is it?

What are you longing for here?

What is it — I don't get it — say it another way.

In all this, what is the central or main issue?

What is your basic assumption in this? What is your cherished notion here? What would happen if you let go of this conditioned notion?

What would you do (say, be) if you wanted to complete this relationship?

What have you never said to me ... that you have withheld ... that has left you incomplete here? Can you say it now? What do you get from not saying it? What is the price you pay?

What do you want in life?

What is your fantasy of what it will take to cure you?

Let yourself gather together a moment quietly. Find the silence within and let what comes be. What comes up?

What's going on with you?

In that situation did you see anything new happening? What was that? What old compulsive conditioned ways were happening? What keeps you attached to them?

Are you avoiding something here with me now?

How do you avoid your anxiety (anger, fear, sadness, etc.) here? What would happen if you lived in it?

What notions of yourself do you cling to?

What thoughts create most misery for you? Why do you hang onto them?

How do you think I am experiencing you now?

What is coming up in you now?

What does this confront you with? What does what you just did (said, experienced) confront you with?

What does this reveal of how you live your life?

How do you perceive how you got to be feeling hurt (etc.) inside?

What still requires finding out?

Is it absolutely necessary that you do this, say this, feel this? How come? What else opens up as alternatives?

Did you write the script on this or did your mother (etc.)?

Have you ever slowed down thinking? What is it to be with yourself then in silence?

What pretense are you putting up now? What for? Can you let it go . . . it is only an idea . . . what makes it difficult to let go of it?

What would it take from inside you to feel more comfortable (happy, etc.) in life?

Is all this absolutely necessary? What other options do you see?

Did you ever forget yourself here? Then what happened?

What do you have in common with other peopl here?

How do you want to change yourself here? What habits will have to be broken . . . how will you break them? What keeps you from breaking them?

How did you put what we found out in therapy into practice?

How do you use what you see in therapy in daily life?

What is this anger, fear, confusion (etc.) you mention?

What is the depression (etc.) as you experience it? Can you come up with an image of it?

What would you imagine saying to him (her, them, etc.) that would give you a sense of fullness?

You want to get better (etc.) – what is better as you see it?

How can we go into this more deeply? What are the basic issues?

1.6 The manner in which a question is asked is crucial

A woman sat talking a mile a minute, going from one thing to another, appearing detached from what she was saying, making sure I did not interrupt. I listened and was silent, even though at times she smiled or gestured for a response. I willfully wanted to change the level of dialogue.

After a moment's pause, I asked, "What do you hear yourself saying in all of this?" The woman langhed and said, "I don't know." I then asked, "Where are you when you are talking?" She mentioned being distracted. "Take all of what you said and see what you were saying."

She began to be quiet and said with some sincerity, "I don't know what I'm talking about. I just can't stop. I don't think I want you to know how stupid I really am. I probably think I have nothing to say." She began to cry a bit and said, "If I stop for a second, I feel lost and sad. I guess I'm trying not to see that, 'cause I don't understand that." I was silent and nodded.

With these few straightforward questions the patient had been directed to look at a deeper process inside herself; she was directed to organize what she was saying. This revealed her sense of fear and how she used words to avoid inner experiencing. *As a person begins to look inward for answers, to reflect more openly from inside, to talk more, there is actual mastery* and thus the feeling of increasing strength that comes with being able to learn to do something. As we encourage our patients to attend, think, and feel by the phrasing of questions, patients *consider questions they never asked themselves or nobody asked them. They discover what it means for someone to be interested in their personal response. They can get interested in themselves and stay with something long enough to discover what they feel or think or intuit or imagine*, which is quite different from what they were conditioned to think or feel by their parents. They discover a new awareness of their internal life, which they were never encouraged to focus on or share with anyone before. Through inquiry and finding inner responses, they find themselves more full, more whole.

We question to enable the patient to have an experience in the telling. Having an inner experience, he has more, is more.

There are basically two types of questions: open-ended and specific. The more open-ended the question, the more loosely organized the field remains and the wider the creative possibilities for response from the patient; the more specific and particular the question, the more it moves the patient into recreating an event. For a patient who is always abstract and talks in generalities, specific questions serve to shift the focus to the more particular. With a patient who is concrete and talks in details, mentioning all that takes place, it is helpful to move to more abstract questions.

To the patient, the questions can mean that the therapist is present, attentive, interested, wants to know more, is moving with him, is granting him permission to understand, to both know and not know. Questions indicate that what the therapist is asking about has value and is worth exploring. Questions convey that the therapy is a mutual, cooperative venture where no one has the answers, that answers are to be discovered together out of caring for one another.

Patients will mistrust, become irritated, and block with questions that focus on what is the matter with them. Patients may find it hard to answer questions when they think there is a correct answer or that not to know immediately means they don't know. Many people are ashamed of how little they have thought things through, or how little they know of their own feelings or thoughts. Some people cannot believe that the therapist does care to hear the answer. Some people do not want to look inwardly or find out much about themselves. All of these possibilities can be gone into with the patient.

However, if questioned with the right attitude of openness and nonevaluation, most people will be inspired to find some answers within. As with anything else, the right timing, quantity, and quality of asking is not a prescription, but emerge out of a sense of what is right with this patient. However, it is also true that many therapists hesitate to ask questions, feeling unsure of what to do with the answers, as if fuller participation in the telling were not the objective. We are working to enable patients to live with wholehearted involvement and our listening and inquiry facilitate this process. Involved responding, where patients are at one with the responding, is the wholeness we seek.

In an article on the use of questions in therapy, Harold Kelman writes, "To me, then, questions are pointers. The therapist is saying, 'I have seen, I am interested. I believe it will be worthwhile if you look in that direction and in that area.' "[12] The question throws light on the area to which the patient is being guided. The question is also a source of support and hence of energy. The patient is responsive to the therapist's implicit urging that he make efforts towards exploration in that area. The therapist is implicitly asking him to be there, be more involved with there, wherever "there" might be.

Throughout therapy the therapist observes and explores how he and the patient live with each other *in the session*. The work of the therapist is to see what takes place and to mention this without being for or against it. In such seeing *we recognize and respect the moment of experience as it is being created. The technique of the therapist concerns finding ways to enable patients to be more aware of the moment as it is taking place. Questions are aimed at what is taking place in the experiencing of the patient in the session.* We ask questions of patients to direct their attention to what they are doing right here and now in the session as a reflection of how they live, and their solutions to or avoidances of conflict out of the session. We see the fixed forms the patient moves into during the session. Questions that focus on the behavior in the session are aimed at reducing dissociation, fragmentation, living with greater awareness of who one is and how one lives, being aware in the Present, increasing constructive differentiation. There are questions that focus on the therapeutic relationship, forms of avoiding, relationship to anxiety, what creates the anxiety in the session. Asking questions about behavior in the session is a way of enabling the patient to be more wholly aware of what is taking place. Here is an example from a session:

A patient was looking around the office with nothing to talk about. I asked how she was today and she smiled and said, "Okay?" This was a question, not a statement. I mentioned the question mark, asking if she wanted me to tell her something. She said that she wanted me to do something for her. There was silence. I asked, "What do you intend to tell me?" She laughed and said that she didn't think that much was happening. I asked her what much would be and she then said that actually she was much better and that she was exaggerating.

She was uneasy. She spoke of something that had gotten better this weekend. I said she appeared anxious after telling me that she was not satisfied . . . and what was going on right now in this saying how things were okay. The patient began to say that it was hard for her to tell me she was not happy with her work with me . . . there was silence. She then went on to talk of something else. I asked her to go into her not being happy with her work with me. Again she spoke in vague ways. I then asked her what was wrong with our work.

She said I was not telling her what to do enough . . . she wanted me to tell her what to do. I said that I would tell her what to do right now. She laughed. I asked how come she was laughing. She said this wasn't what I was supposed to do. I was just supposed to ask questions and then make interpretations, but that was all based on the past. She wanted to know what to do about her boyfriend. I asked her what specific question she wanted answered. She said, "Should I marry him?" I was silent and then asked, "What do you want in this relationship?" She said, "I don't know. I need someone to tell me. I don't know." I said, "You don't feel anything of what to do." She said, "I don't feel. I don't feel love for him or hate or dislike or like. I don't feel." I asked, "And you want out of this inner condition as it is painful?" I asked, "Live with the not feeling until you have some feeling; how is this?"

Then she moved into talking of how she would not change. She had been unfeeling most of her life . . . it was hopeless. She began to get angry. She began to demand that I help her to feel. She said that everything she had tried had been a waste. I suggested that we just see where she went with her not feeling . . . . And then she got red in the face and said, "Do you think I'm a machine doing what you say? Because you say it, I do it? Where do you go with your feeling . . . bullshit."

I said that when she began to let herself be a bit she could feel, and then blamed me for this as it was something she couldn't permit herself to do: to feel. I asked how come it was not okay in her book to feel or to feel angry. We began to discuss this. Many of her neurotic difficulties came up for observation right in the session as they do with all patients *who live their life in the session as they do out of the session.*

1.7 Moving into the fragment with questions and facilitating new connections to oneself

Let us see how the therapist *moves into the fragment by laying down new connections* to create a larger whole. In this example, the fragment is the patient's idea that he is his parents' slave, which is exemplified to him by his cleaning the basement. Here the therapist moves with the patient's way of seeing something in a fragmented way and opens awareness to greater wholeness. In doing this the therapist must be alert and observant to any changes in the patient — content where there may be some shifts, his face, body, manner which would indicate a less negative sense of himself and his life or some actual movement.

A 27-year-old male is seen in an outpatient clinic. For a short while he sometimes came in without an appointment and sat around saying he didn't know when his appointment was. Later he said it was the only place he knew to go to get out of his parents' house. Prior to seeing this therapist, this man's thoughts were blocked, there was almost no connection between events, his affect was flat, and he felt hopeless about finding a job. He wasn't sure why he came to therapy, only that his parents were worried that he didn't have a job, that he hadn't worked in over two years, that he had no interests, that he had lost many jobs.

In the first 25 sessions there was a stream of negativity and hopelessness and confusion. He showed not one ray of hope that anything could ever reach him. He mentioned feeling lonely in this country – he had no friends; he had come to the United States only 8 years ago; occasionally he visited his father at a foreign-speaking radio station, went to church but never met anyone, had to get a job. He mentioned previous job failure, lack of interest in anything, being afraid, failing at all things.

He then began to talk of feeling ashamed while talking about his life as his mother made a "slave" out of him in the house and he felt obliged to follow her orders. In one session the patient mentioned that he had even cleaned the cellar over the week-end. The therapist noted that there was a slight change of affect here with the first hint of enthusiasm creeping into the patient's voice, although verbally he complained of this as an example of his mother's domination and how he wasted his life.

I asked the supervisee what the patient said about the cellar and she replied: "He said, 'I put the cellar in order.'" I suggested that she focus specifically on what went on in the cellar. Specific questions – what exactly was put in order, what was in the cellar – might open up new feeling connections to some objects in the cellar or to his working there. After the next session the therapist described the patient's talking of how he cleans his desk in the basement, and how he does this with regularity. She said his affect was more alert, unlike other times. This was as far as the therapist went.

I suggested she ask specific questions: "Where did you get the desk?" "How did you happen to get it?" "What does the desk look like, wood drawers, etc.?" "What do you keep in the desk?" I suggested the therapist explore further each item mentioned. For example, if he mentioned a paper, what was on it, was it his, what life events were connected to what was on this paper, what was his experience of these events, etc. I suggested that she focus her questions, specifically on what went on in the cellar and the desk, as this was the only place thus far where the patient appeared alert and able to feel that he could initiate action that interested him. The cellar was the "foundation, the bottom, the beginning, the womb."

With specific questions the patient was quite responsive. The therapist had found something important to the patient and he wanted to share it. The desk was 12 years old. The patient and his father had bought it together. This opened up the area of his relationship to his father, and it emerged that he drove his father's car, shared his father's love of books, read poetry on his father's radio show. This led further to his father's broadcasting, his own childhood in a foreign country during the war as different foreign groups came in, the takeover by the Communists, the persecution of certain political parties, his own writing of poetry. Specific questions about his interest in canoeing, his love of the outdoors, nature, and boats; his dream of living in Canada and visiting an uncle in Ottawa; many feelings towards trees, being in the woods, sitting in the sun, an island in his country, "a hill," "green patches."

I suggested the therapist stay with the desk and ask more about what was in it.

The patient finally was able to share that he kept his poems there, how he was both proud and ashamed of them, how he read one on the radio, the events and people the poems were connected to, how he was so different from his father, a "productive engineer," while he was a dreamer afraid of people, tied to the house and his parents' friends. I suggested the therapist explore qualitative feelings in the basement, e.g., the feel of the desk, sitting at it, the smells, the noises, the quiet, the images that came up there. This patient then began to share some of his inner feeling states of wanting a sense of peace, how this was connected with being around his mother, not his father, his fear of people and how this related to his war experience, etc.

From the statement "I clean the cellar," the patient was able through specific questions to discover connections between himself and others, himself and the events in his life, himself and his present, his past, and his future. Prior to going into what specifically happened in the cellar, the patient was as lost and disorganized in the therapy session as outside of it. By specifically focusing in an area of the patient's actual interest, the questions provided the structure needed by this very withdrawn man so that he could find some interest and sense of mastery in his participation in life.

More disturbed patients tend to be unsure and imitative in what they say. With such patients we look for where their comments feel more genuine and explore this:

A patient who had been hospitalized briefly and was living in a halfway house, spoke with bitterness about his father's coming to visit him. His tone of bitterness was sincere and intense. He reported no movement in their relationship, nothing ever happening. He was totally negative in words, but emotionally involved. Repeatedly he said that he had no relationship with his father. He talked of how they hadn't spoken to each other since a certain event before his hospitalization. He described feeling numb with his father. He defined himself by the fragment, "I have nothing with my father."

In our sessions I chose to explore what had happened to him when he and his father stopped speaking since there was sincere interest and emotional involvement instead of compulsive negativism when it came up. He described how he had asked his father repeatedly for financial support so that he could go to school, and his father had ignored his requests. After release from the hospital, he drove to his father's place, knocked on the door, and said, "What are you going to do for me?" He expressed his rage at his father, his father expressed his anger at him.

Here I explored the particular details of this interaction to open up the patient's experience. I encouraged him to see his capacity to be active, his anger, his hurt, his seeing more who is father was, etc. I questioned his willingness to question and see the relationship and his awareness of his feelings. I questioned his wish to be friendly and gentle with his fear. My questions helped clarify that the patient struggles to face the actuality of the nature of his father's caring. It is for this reason that he now avoids seeing his father, talking to him, and pretends they have no relationship rather than a relationship of pain and conflict and caring.

I pointed out that this avoidance of anger is a very active process. He chooses not to see his father as he is and denies that they have a relationship. I mentioned his difficulty now with separating from his father and his holding on to his anger. I discussed both his difficulty letting go into his anger, and his courage in doing this. Thus we found a process where there is a definite relationship, one reflecting avoidance, denial, splitting, projection, a long history of fear of separate existence as well as one where he confronted his father, indicating an increased strength to endure anxiety and rage. There was a healthy wish to be more autonomous combined with a fear of this. I inquired and looked at the process with his father and he saw the depth of their relationship. Aided by direct inquiry for specifics in an area where he had tried to deny, the patient felt stronger and relieved that he could go through this process of knowing what he felt, living and acting in it. Once seeing the pain and living in it, being it, it passed and the patient opened to several new positive connections to his father. In our inquiry he had discovered his own vicissitudes which he had fragmented and fixed prior to our work.

The objective of these questions is to enable a person to be connected with what is taking place, to achieve the reduction of suffering. When you are wholly being what is happening, there is no "you" to comment on it. Being connected with the event is the very liberation from it. Being the dreaded feeling without separation is what is going to enable you to end it. I say "I" am afraid to be sad, but when I am wholly sad there is no "I" and then the feeling changes to another state of mind. In this connection with the inner event there is the elimination of separation, and the end of thinking about it. In being it, you are not making any evaluation of it, there is no "you" to make judgment, there is no commenting on it: duality is gone, there is only pure living. It is this connection to what is taking place which is the greatest healing therapy has to offer. It is based on the experience that when you are being what is happening "it" will not exist, for at that level of whole participation there is no sense of any "it"; there is just the experience. It is my thinking about it, my separation from it that keeps it going. It is to break through the separation from the inner event that we find ways to connect the individual with his thoughts and feelings so that he can experience them deeply and then be free of them.

Questions thus serve to move the person into the event, to participate in it more openly and wholly, then to finally be it, to where it ends and something new can begin. In this way he learns how to free himself from fear by being what he fears. For most people, the actual event is never so bad as the idea.

1.8 Clarifying actuality

Asking for details, for particulars, for more of what took place brings more clarity to a formerly fragmented view. Clarifying actuality creates greater wholeness in one's inner life. A major event occurs as the patient clarifies the actuality. He eventually stops longing for things to be different than they are. He takes the world as it is a bit more. He is then more whole and sound, more connected to events and himself as they are. As actuality fills out for the patient, new inner connections are laid down in the form of new feelings, images, dreams, etc.; awareness opens and expands. There is more of a felt sense of being whole within the patient which may or may not be mentioned. The actual inner or outer event is whole. The patient begins by seeing only a fragment of that totality. We ask questions that enable the patient to discover more of the whole way it was experienced inside as well as more of the whole way it was perceived from outside.

1.9 Where to work outside the compulsive fragment

Frank wants to write a novel, but in the meantime he can't concentrate or think straight. What he can do is work in public relations and have relationships on the job. With me he says he wants to work on his writing.

The actuality as we talk is that he is too anxious to write. When he sits down at the typewriter he is distracted, thinking of thousands of things, among them that his kids are making noise, how he hates his wife, how he has nothing worthy to say, or something so powerful to say that he is frozen by its magnitude. He strays off into thinking of his friends, what he hasn't done, how he is wasting his life, how he must write to justify his existence. Then he drinks a few beers and becomes fuzzy and unable to think. This had gone on for several years. He has never completed anything he has written. He has never written what he wants to write nor can be do it at this time. This is what emerges as the actuality.

I realize this but do not mention his compulsive need to fulfill an image that has nothing to do with who he is in fact. What Frank can do is to care deeply about his son; there are difficulties there so we talk of this. As he mentions what happens in the office, I explore his holding this job, getting something from it, and being interested in it even though he doesn't think he should be.

As we talk of his son, their similarities and differences, it was clear that this was one person he can feel for, share with, does not hate, does not feel is using him. He wants to give to his son, and as therapy progresses, he is able to be more giving. He is also more able to be disciplined in the office, not to lose his temper. He is given a small promotion and stops abusing his wife.

Each weekend he still sits at the typewriter and writes little. As he is given more responsibility on his actual job, the need to sit for six hours at the typewriter lessens to where he spends his first weekend in five years with his wife and son without feeling a sense of failure for not writing. After one year, Frank says, "I will let the writing go for a while, until I have something I have to say . . . and I think that will come."

Realizing that this man actually could not write his novel moved me to work with him on what he could do right now. In this way he was able to free himself of the rigid image that he had to be a writer. If at the time of entry I had worked with him on his drinking patterns, his constant distractions, his violence with his wife and family, his writing, I would have created more feeling of failure, and I believe he would have terminated psychotherapy. Here we worked to clarify the actuality *outside the compulsive fragment*, "I have to be a writer," until he could find inside himself what he wanted in his life at this point rather than what he compulsively had to do to fulfill a false notion of himself.

Once we see actuality we can stop longing for it to be another way: in this we are more whole.

A patient was furious that her boss was was dumb and unrealistically demanding. She was continually outraged with this boss who could not teach her what she needed to know. She was getting nothing on the job because of this boss. For months she described the various dumb, stupid, insensitive things this man had done in vivid detail, each time feeling frustrated and hurt or angry and helpless. She wanted to stay on the job but every contact with his man produced rage. Every week there was something new about this boss.

I said, "You and I agree that this man is dumb. How can you keep expecting him to be otherwise?" The patient saw this with resounding clarity. She laughed. She said, "I want him to be another way than the way he is. That's what everybody always wanted from me. It's the same with my mother. Over and over I'm disgusted that she gives me food to take home like I'm a kid. A million times I told her not to and a million times she doesn't hear me. Why can't I digest this?" The patient at last felt more relaxed at work; having seen the actuality, she did not expect the boss to be different.

At the moment when there is an awareness of the actuality, there is relief, even if there is also suffering. You may not be better, but you are where it's happening. The relief comes from removing the ignorance we have of who we are and participating in being who we are. We remove the strain of fictitious being.

An extremely chaotic patient who frantically moves from one job to another, one relationship to another, one idea of herself to another, has been in a love relationship for almost a year. This is the longest relationship she has sustained in her 26 years. She has described with some feeling (unusual for her) how she cannot enjoy sex with the women she feels she loves. She is revolted by certain aspects of love-making and forces herself to do them, but her lover sees that she is forcing. The patient wants me to tell her what to do. She describes the love-making in obsessive detail and fragments this aspect off from the rest of the relationship, deluding herself into thinking that the rest is fine.

Her lover threatens separation. The patient's pressure in therapy increases. She accuses me of not helping. I say, "As I see it, the actual place you are in right now is not knowing what to do. This is a perfectly valid place to be. And one issue is seeing how things are in fact. The fact is you don't know what to do." The patient listens, is silent, and says nastily, "That I could have told myself. I don't have to come here to find out I don't know what to do." I say, "You have to see how it is first before you can change it. How it is is a deep sense of not knowing what to do. That's what it is. Let that soak in. Don't fight seeing what actually is." The patient leaves, being sarcastic about how I always say the obvious.

At the next session she is appreciative for the first time in two years. She says, "Last week what you said really helped. I said to Laura when we were in bed, 'I just don't know what to do.' And I meant it. And she said she didn't know what to do either. And then we just hugged each other and held each other and we didn't have sex. It was the warmest we've ever been with each other in a long time. I don't know why but I feel better about the whole thing." The patient then goes on to discuss some interpersonal problem she has with her lover which does not involve sex, and seems generally more sharing and real. She clearly sees more of the whole of the relationship following some clarification of actuality.

When the therapist can observe the actuality of who the patient is, he stops longing for the patient to be different. This is what parents could not do.

Clare was extremely nasty – continually. I began to dread seeing her. She was adept at picking at my vulnerabilities. I saw her projections, her transference, saw at times her pain, but I was worn out and angry for sessions.

Then she came in with a more genuine tone. She said, "I can't stand it when George speaks to anyone else, anyone. I'm always afraid he'll walk out. I feel so afraid. (silence) I don't think you see how afraid I am. (silence.)" I looked and saw her hands trembling very mildly. She was afraid of me, too. I said nothing but was with her in her fear, feeling it, being with her experience. There was a deep sigh and then I sighed too.

She went on. "I'm so jealous of George's life, every breath is a personal attack on me. Nothing ever gets solved. I feel I have nothing in my life that counts, and every time he's interested I think he'll find out how dead I am . . . and then I get scared that I'll be left. (long pause) Do you hear how scared I am?" I said yes and felt it. She was quiet, then went on to say that in two weeks there was to be a party in George's office. "I thought of going, although I never go . . . What I thought of was what I would wear, but I told George I didn't want to go. I can't go because I'm possessed with envy. But . . . I might go. I might not." I said that she felt she had options, and she agreed.

In this session I was aware of the *movement* in Clare's feeling of having no options in her compulsive jealousy to a new sense of having options about the party. In my interpretation to her I focused *on this movement*. Her experiencing the actuality of her fear in this session, living with it, my recognizing the meaning of it, imparting it to her and letting her be, led to a greater sense of internal strength and flexibility to where she felt she had options. As the session ended there was a new feeling between us of having been somewhere together. She was able to open to new possibilities because I saw her fear and became one with it. In doing this, I no longer wished for her to be different. This is, then, when my empathy could begin.

Therapy is concerned with a discovery of what is. You cannot know what to do until you know what is actually going on. In exploring the actual, the therapist keeps on the track of not what would be better or different or should be, but of inquiring into how things are in fact. It is the avoidance of seeing what is that creates misery. It is living in what is that creates greater connection to oneself.

Jack was a patient in a day hospital therapy group of which I was the leader. He was 42 years old, had never had close friends, and had been hospitalized at the point when he was successful on his first job. Then he felt he could not "keep up with it" and admitted himself to the hospital. Jack's life was wrapped up in the thought fragment that he was a cripple and disgusting since he had had polio and had a bad arm. No one could move him from the position that he was repulsive until he began to enjoy the good humor of the group somewhat. In a state of increased participation one day, he admitted that he enjoyed going to the horse races, something he had kept a secret before. He didn't want anyone to know that in fact he didn't hide out in his apartment all weekend.

He didn't know why but the actuality of his having some fun bothered him until he saw that he was literally trained to be an invalid by his mother, who waited on him hand and foot. She insisted that Jack keep his arm covered. She always told him that girls would not want him.

Jack was well aware of how much he hated his mother. His rages with his mother were ongoing with both of them beating each other, throwing things, leaving home. Three years before joining the group, his mother moved to Florida, and Jack found himself feeling better. He joined the Y and began to swim, and he became closer to his brother. He did not miss his mother, who came up to see her boys once a year. Each time she had come in the past, Jack had been upset with migraine headaches.

This year at her announced visit, Jack had called his brother and told him that he couldn't keep her, although she supported him and paid the rent on the apartment so that she could stay there when she came to New York. In the group, Jack felt a false sense of inflation commenting on this call. He denied his brother's response of not wanting his mother either. Jack then suggested to the group that he meet his mother at the airport and take her to a hotel. There was a consensus that this was a good idea.

I asked Jack to imagine for a moment meeting his mother at the airport and then seeing her, giving me a description of her, which he did. I said, "Now imagine yourself telling her that you are going to take her to a hotel." Jack immediately put his head in his hands, saying, "I don't . . . I can't do it." The group said, "Yes you can," etc. I asked, "Jack, take a good look at the actuality. What is it you can do and what is it you do in fact?" He said that he could take his mother to their apartment and continue to have headaches. There was general silence. I said that this was how it was, but that since he had some friends now, this year he might be able to find some understanding of how hard it was to be with his mother, that he might feel the experience differently since he had some people to share it with. Jack agreed and said, "I've been kidding myself for weeks. But not really. I don't know why I don't have a headache just thinking of it, but I don't."

What is helpful is to work where the patient knows that he is seeing what he knew all along and had to ignore, thus pretending to himself and creating tension. It is the disconnection from actuality that creates the pain in this patient's head.

How do we enable the patient to be more aware of his connections with the therapist, to be more connected, less separated with other peoople? This is what we shall discuss next.

References

1. Karen Horney, *Neurosis and Human Growth* (New York: W. W. Norton & Company, 1950), pp. 156–57.
2. Louis Breger, "Anxiety, Dissociation and the Growth of Self," *From Instinct to Identity*, (Englewood Cliffs, N. J.: Prentice-Hall, 1974), p. 194.
3. James F. Masterson, *Psychotherapy of the Borderline Adult* (New York: Brunner Mazel, 1976), p. 103.
4. Tarthang Tulku, *Openness Mind* (Berkeley: Dharma Publishing, 1978).
5. Shunryu Suzuki, *Zen Mind, Beginner's Mind* (New York and Tokyo: John Weatherhill Inc., 1970).
6. D. W. Winnicott, *The Maturational Processes and the Facilitating Environment* (New York: International Universities Press, 1965), p. 223.
7. Heinz Kohut, *The Analysis of the Self* (New York: International Universities Press, 1971), pp. 123–24.
8. M. Masud R. Khan, *The Privacy of the Self* (New York: International Universities Press, 1974), p. 44.
9. Diane Shainberg, "Work with Imagination in the Treatment of Borderline Patients," *Journal of the American Academy of Psychoanalysis*, Vol. 7, no. 3, 419–435, 1979.
10. Gerald Epstein, M. D., *Waking Dream Therapy* (New York: Human Sciences Press, 1981).
11. Shunryu Suzuki, *op. cit.*, p. 75.
12. Harold Kelman, "Irrational Feelings: A Therapeutic Approach," *Comprehensive Psychiatry*, Vol. 14, 218, May-June 1973.

IV. Facilitating Connections to the Therapist: The Disposition of Mind that Heals

A human relationship created the mental disturbance we see in our office; a human relationship can heal the disturbance. Psychiatry has not given enough emphasis to the healing power of the organism in relationship.

My years of being a supervisor have convinced me that the thoughts and feelings of the therapist often prevent the patient from discovering who he is in certain dimensions because they are too threatening to the therapist over time. I have seen therapists with long analyses and with a good theoretical grasp unable to work when someone is consistently angry with them. I have supervised therapists who went out socially with their patients, one therapist who had sex with a patient, one therapist who did not charge a patient for two years and could not ask for money. I have seen therapists trapped for years in what looked like a close relationship with the patient where the therapist could not stay with anything in the realm of despair. All of these therapists were aware of their feelings and could not break out of the transformation with the patient because of their own needs from the patient. Personal psychoanalysis does not always enable the therapist to be consistently empathic with patients who make deep emotional demands on them. When we are upset we find ways to avoid pain at the expense of the patient. When we are thrown we find a collusive way to work: I won't upset you if you won't upset me so much.

It is now time to focus on the mind of the therapist so that he will not be so dependent and so thrown by patients. I think we have minimized how much our own needs for external security and satisfaction have blocked the work we do with certain patients. I think we are nowhere near being able to be consistently empathic with many of the patients we see. I am not saying that it is inappropriate at times to be angry or hopeless or confused with patients, but when these feeling states and avoidance of them are prominent in the therapy over time, we must consider why psychoanalysis has not resolved this. How can we attain unqualified compassion . . . or consistent empathy? I would like not only to be aware of countertransference, but when it keeps me from being open with the patient, I also want to resolve it. I think Eastern spiritual teachings and practice offer us some guidance towards gaining a mind that is able to be and remain open to people. And it is the mind of the therapist that is a primary factor in facilitating healing.

1.1 The Disposition of Mind that Heals

Denial of the connection with one's fellow man is accompanied by psychological illness. In their contact with one another, all men find meaning. The oneness between people is a fundamental state, not an accomplishment. What is necessary for the oneness to unfold is the right persons and the right environment where there is space to be oneself, to find oneself, to express oneself openly without being hurt.

Who is the person able to be the guide in this process of finding wholeness, finding movement, finding connection with oneself and the world? If we wish to enable another person to be whole, we must be whole ourselves in knowing the whole of who we are, including the various levels of mind. We must know the mind in silence or emptiness, in experience without concepts and with concepts. Without this knowledge *in* the mind, the therapist is not whole himself.

Let us look at the disposition of mind that can heal, the inner condition of the therapist who can work with all kinds of mentally upset people and not find himself upset. It is my clinical experience that the consciousness of the person who can heal, can facilitate change, is different than that of the ordinary person and yet deeply appreciative of the ordinary. The therapist who facilitates healing is one who has consistent experience with a level of mind where he has found peace, fullness, completion within himself. He knows a level of mind which could be called the source of thoughts and feelings. This level of mind is calm and characterized not by thought, but by silence, awareness, emptiness of craving. At this place, there is peace and completion, the end of the wanting mind.

Knowing this level of mind, the healer as therapist is not dependent on others for the source of his fullness. He sees how thoughts come and go and does not attach to them; likewise feelings. From this Silence or Source, he sees and feels the inherent goodness of all of his patients, of all men, who when they contact this level of mind, are themselves what they are seeking. It is experience with this level of mind which gives the therapist the openness in seeing how other people are in fact without likes and dislikes. This is the source of compassionate openness.

The reactive mind of the therapist is not only a source of countertransference, but also the major obstacle in facilitating human change. If he is to be a facilitator of change, the therapist must transform his consciousness. We know that psychological knowledge alone does not lead to empathy. It is my opinion that knowledge from Eastern spiritual teachings can enable us to have new experiences of the self which will lead to more openness and empathy in the work of psychotherapy, and will thus facilitate healing in our patients.

*   *   *

Let us recall this quotation from M. Masud Khan[1] as a way of looking at the work of psychotherapy:

The real task is to enable the patient to experience regressively and affectively in the analytic setting the total fragmented reality that he is carrying around under magical control, and work through it from within by experiencing the new emergent relationship to himself, the analyst and the analytic situation. *This means that the reality and limitation of the analyst as a person are bound to become more visible in the process . . . . The real difference between this analytic experience and the social experiences for the patient is that in the analytic experience the patient is able to exteriorize and express all the facets and elements of his current and developmental experiences* without magically seducing the analyst into collusion or rejection. This ability to be involved without interfering with the inner logic of the patient's growing reality is the most delicate task. (p.25)

We say that it is important for the patient to express "all the facets and elements of his current and developmental experiences without magically seducing the analyst into collusion or rejection." However, in order to bear the weight of all the elements of the human being, we have to be able to live in the presence of hatred, despair, confusion, bewilderment, terror, hopelessness, bitterness, voracious demands, joy, creativity, love, etc. If these elements throw the therapist, we rob the patient of the ability to get to know and to experience new aspects of himself that will lead to his being more whole. What is the knowledge and experience of the mind that can live comfortably in the presence of *all the facets and elements* of any person without being upset continually? This is the question we have to address as therapists, for without being able to be inwardly free, to give patients the freedom to be *all* these ways, the therapy becomes just another situation where the patient must learn to react to a set of demands, different from the parents' but nonetheless geared to the comfort and satisfaction of another. Without being given the freedom *to be, to exist as is*, over time, the patient cannot become more authentic and will not be able to discover or express who he truly is.

The disposition of mind that heals includes knowledge of the whole of *who I am*. It sees that all thoughts and feelings are of equal valence. It knows that the mind creates all problems and that the world is objective. It knows through experience that the therapist and others are the same at the deepest level, that our true nature is identical . . . whether it is called Buddha nature, Silence Awareness, or The Way. What the therapist thinks and feels is the ambience that Winnicott calls "the facilitating environment." The therapist's mind is the facilitating environment. In such an environment, the ignorance of who we truly are drops away. The healer has experienced the level of mind outside of sensation, craving, and thought many times, and knows this level of experience as his Self. He does not define himself only by his individual ego characteristics, with its thoughts and feelings, just as he does not totally define himself by his name and form. Rather, he identifies with what is common to all mankind, a level of mind where there is pure awareness, infinite, complete, there is no adding to, no taking away. At the level of the mind in Silence Awareness, there is the peace we seek. It is the source of our life. There is no being thrown at this level.

The holistic healer locates and experiences the self at a different level than the individual ego. He has addressed the question "Who am *I*?" and has found a level of self that is silent, empty of thought and craving, full and complete.

In *Buddhist Meditation*, Edward Conze[2] says:

The assumption is made that our mind consists of two disparate parts — a depth which is calm and quiet, and a surface which is disturbed. The surface layer is in perpetual turmoil. There exists, however, a centre which is quiet still, at the bottom of the mind, beyond both the conscious and the unconscious mind as modern psychologists understand it. The turmoil is caused by three agents: 1) the senses 2) the passions, wants and desires and 3) discursive thinking.

These are the three enemies of spiritual quietude. The holistic therapist has experienced the end of craving, the end of discursive thinking, and the withdrawal of the senses from their objects so that a peace has been achieved, not touched by the turmoil of conflict of everyday life. This process may have occurred in therapy at moments of healing, or in spiritual practice. Conze further says:

In many persons, the depth is overlaid to such an extent by turmoil that they remain quite incredulous when told of a submerged spot of stillness in the inmost being.

In order to be freer of the reactive mind, the holistic therapist has often participated in some spiritual reading, teaching, or practice that describes experiences different from our everyday ego existence. Having learned in meditation practice, and letting go in therapy, that he has what he needs inside to be full and happy, he does not rely on external objects such as patients to bring him a sense of completion or security. Only in this knowledge can the therapist be free of using the patient for his own reactive needs. Only through experience with physical, emotional, mental, and spiritual phenomena, is the therapist whole and free to let people be who they are in all the realms of their existence.

Webster defines *spirit* as ' the animating or vital principle in man." It is what exists when there are no concepts attached to a thing. The spirit cannot be described, it does not have qualities because it exists at a level where there is no thought. It is what is experienced with no concepts. In Zen Buddhist literature, this way of perceiving is called seeing "suchness." It is seeing the person free of one's own concepts. This way of perceiving the person is essential to the holistic therapist, for without it the patient is perceived as the characteristics, readings, supervisions, and other patients in the therapist's mind.

Lao Tzu said: "Yield and you need not break. Bent you can straighten. Emptied you can hold." (Verse 22) The therapist we are discussing has many times experienced "emptied you can hold" in his own analysis, or in spiritual practice, and work with patients.

Consciousness is the moment-by-moment flow of thoughts and feelings that give rise to further thoughts and feelings. This is not the nature of my deepest Self. Where then do I locate the "I"? A brief meditation that follows from the Vedanta, or Hindu tradition, may help to conceive this[3] :

The word . . . "I"
"I"
What is
   the meaning of the word
   I . . . ?
The sun is known . . .
   it is not I.
   I is the knower.
The moon is known . . .
   it is not I.
   I is the knower.
This body is known . . .
   it is not I.
   "I" is the knower.
The breath is known . . .
   it is not "I."
   "I" is the knower.
The knower . . . is not known

the knower . . .
is . . .
. . . Awareness
. . . .

. . . .
Awareness . . . "I" . . .
Awareness . . . "I"
Awareness . . . "I"
Awareness

This knowledge the therapist has of this level of the mind outside duality, outside disquietude, enables him to witness thoughts and feelings and not be thrown by them. The therapist knows this next meditation from repeated inner experience, and it is part of what he never forgets as a means of knowing the *I* for all people. It is a knowledge he brings to his work in healing in psychotherapy.

I hear the various sounds . . . .
As I hear them . . . I don't react.
    I remain Awareful.
Awareful in the ears . . . I hear sounds –
    the sounds don't disturb me.
I am Awareful . . . in the ears.
In Awareness they are heard. . . .
    they keep on disappearing. . . .
    and the new sounds are heard.
I don't know what sound I am going to hear . . .
    it may be of a bird . . .
    but . . .
I am Awareful as the sounds are heard . . . I don't react.
This is the abiding mind . . . .
    This is the greatest form of concentration . . . .
    This is Attention . . . .
I keep hearing the sounds.
The Silent Awareness
That I Am
    is undisturbed – unshaken.
I Am the Silent Awareness . . . I am Awareful Silence.
    Silent Awareness,
    I Am Silent Awareness . . .

When I repeatedly have this experience of knowing who I am at this level of Silent Awareness, then this knowledge brings me the fullness that I seek. I will see that *just this very moment* is all there is in life and it is complete just as it is even though it may be full of pain. It enables me to be more consistently empathic as I will not be clouded with needs for the patient to be any particular way.

To be a person who can create wholeness, to unify another without being thrown by the facades of the patient, we have to know and have the experience that leads to faith that under all the thinking and feeling facades, the pretenses, masks, protections, *is* the Buddha nature, is the full, complete, peaceful person we seek – not because I or any other teacher told you this, but because you have gone through your own way of finding this out and have come to this inner peace over and over, this common root which is quiescence on your own or with a spiritual teacher or therapist.

The therapist who can heal knows intimately through experience that level of mind where there is peace and fullness, the Silence Awareness which is the source of all thought and feeling. Thus the healer does not take himself to be only his thoughts and feelings. He is calmly able to watch these forms pass through consciousness, not getting upset by them, as he does not identify who he is with them. He knows that who he is, his sense of "I," does not occur exclusively at the ego level. This means that he is not thrown by thoughts and feelings. When a difficult thought comes up, he is able to watch it and to know that he is the watcher, not "it." The level of mind at which he experiences his deepest sense of Self is where there is the Silence that leads to empathy, the Silence Awareness in which all men share. The therapist as healer is also able to have direct experience in which there are no concepts at the intuitive level, and to have images without concepts. He also knows the interpretations of experience where there are concepts, but he sees how these concepts are far removed from direct experience. As Tarthang Tulka has clearly discussed in *Openness Mind*, "At the level of concepts, we focus on meaning, but one meaning is explained by another meaning, as in the dictionary. When we do not assign meanings to anything but see things and allow things to be simply as they are we discover in them their intrinsic nature."

The healer is thus able to see things without imagining they are the same as his concepts. The word is not the thing. So he is asking, "Who is this person without any concepts? Can I see the person without my concepts? Only then can I see him. If not, I can see and hear only my concepts of him." In knowing this level of mind or self where there is Silence Awareness, the therapist knows from consistent experience that we are all the fullness we are seeking. Because of this experience of self, the therapist is not dependent on patients for what he needs in life and is thus able to be open with them, to be non-reactive much of the time, and is truly able to live openly and peaceably with how they are as is . . . not needing them or himself to be different.

I think that there are many times when we move outside of duality in therapy, when we participate so wholly that we lose the sense of who we are. To find the self is to lose the self. It happens when we let go of our efforts and simply are what is happening. It happens when we can be the experience and not separate from it by commenting on it. It happens when we try and try and see that trying will not help, and then let go into the silence in which we simply are what is taking place. In therapy we get glimpses of what it means not to be separated from ourselves, not watching, not self-conscious, not thinking about it, when we are thoroughly involved in the moment. These are moments of healing in which we realize that what we seek is to be found inside.

The experience with this level of mind of Silence Awareness can occur in therapy with a therapist who sees the importance of the work as enabling the patient to participate fully in the moment, so that separation from himself ends. In this wholehearted participation and absorption, there is no "I" watching . . . there is simply being the event. In this way, to participate fully in the moment is to end the misery that our avoiding and commenting on the moment creates.

In spiritual practice we are told that to end our suffering is to end the mind that is reactive and to learn that *when all things are seen in the equal mind they return to their nature.*[7]

If the mind makes no discriminations, all things are as they really are.[8]

Human goodness is a fact in all spiritual traditions: Give man freedom and he will be his true nature, which is good.

Therefore a sensible man says[9]:
> If I keep from meddling with people, they take care of themselves
> If I keep from commanding people, they behave themselves
> If I keep from preaching at people, they improve themselves
> If I keep from imposing on people, they become themselves.

This is a quite different perspective from psychoanalysis, which sees man in perpetual conflict which comes out of his ego's being taken as his whole self. This misperception separates him from other men, and he perpetually feels he must attain reunion.

However, although we come to see in therapy that we are inwardly what we have always sought outwardly, the ability to sustain this realization is often transient. We find that certain thoughts and feelings still can control us. We find ourselves ruled by the mind that has likes and dislikes and is always discriminating. In this situation, we may either accept happiness as transitory or continue efforts to end our suffering by seeking a spiritual teaching and practice which we hope will give us a more sustained sense of contact with our intrinsic nature.

It is a pathological process when we take ourselves to be only our thoughts and feelings. When a person says "I am depressed" and defines himself in this way, he is attaching to this emotion and clinging to it, thinking this is the whole of who he is. He is telling us that he is giving this more valence and not paying attention to the many other ways that he feels. He is also telling us that he is constricted in his awareness of the other ways that he feels. Defining the self by certain thoughts or feelings means being controlled by them, to think mistakenly that We are Them.

Our work is to find ways to enable patients to let go of notions that create misery. Our work is to find way to connect the individual to new aspects of himself outside compulsive thought and feeling. We also explore how these thoughts and feelings open or close possibilities for the patient . . . and we see how the event itself of depression or not being able to do it is not nearly so terrible as all the thoughts we have *about it*, the comments we make on it. It is the commentary that creates human suffering. Our problem then is that we take ourselves to be different than we actually are. When we see that there is an "I" witnessing these thoughts and feelings . . . a different "I", then we can at least see that this is not the whole of who we are. When the therapist looks at the question of "Who am I?" he has found the answer in a larger sense of wholeness than the patient who defines himself by the fragment. We ask a person, "Are you your arm?" and there is laughter, but when we ask, "Are you the person who is not loved?" the patient responds often with "Yes." This is the thought fragment to which he clings and he does not allow into consciousness other thoughts, or if he has them, he does not consider them valid. To connect a patient to himself is to open up this process of taking oneself to be only one's thoughts and feelings and to see the limited value and the falseness in this process. The healer does not define himself by his thoughts and feelings. When he asks, "Who am I," he locates the "I" in a different level of the mind. He sees the whole of who he is: with silence awareness and no concepts, with experience and no concepts, and with concepts. Knowing the whole of who I am, I am then able to see the limited way patients who are ignorant of the levels of self live perpetually upset and thrown by life's events.

At the level of the self where the therapist locates the "I" there is no conflict, and there is no separation from other people since we all share in the Silence Awareness of the universe out of which our individual names and forms emerge. At the ego level, there is understanding of our individuality, but this very sense of being individual and separate is both positive and negative, for the sense of individuality, the sense that we have a separate ego, results in the separation from others and the fear of others. At the ego level, there is often a belief and feeling that the world does not care but must be cajoled or dominated. So with the self defined at the ego level, suffering is inherent to the human condition. In this separate ego situation there is continual comparison of this illusory self with other separate selves.

Maintaining this separateness, these fragments, requires energy. One is continually exhausted from the effort of sustaining barriers. One's energies are dissipated. In therapy, we separate patient from therapist, then further separate person from diagnosis, type of therapy, training of therapist, social worker, psychologist. We separate the mind from the heart, the head from the body, the mind from the spirit, the self from other selves. All this business. Where is there a breathing space for pure awareness, for pure openness in therapy? At the level at which the holistic therapist locates the deepest self, there is no separation between people, there is no discrimination, no likes and dislikes, only the silent awareness out of which and in which all people exist in inner peace and freedom.

The calm, quiet and peaceful mind that one reaches in meditation is the state of mind in which there is no wanting and no judging of what happens. In meditation, we are taught not to attach to any thought. We do not interpret thought. When fear comes, we simply let it come and go. The fear comes, but since we do not take it to be who we are, since we do not comment on it, it goes. When we do not equate it with our self-image, it goes away. This non-reaction to what comes up teaches us to be able to move with whatever comes up in life, without attaching to it, watching it without judgment.

When we remain attached to certain self-image concepts, we are thrown by patients. This can happen only when we do not experience on a daily basis in Silence that we are the very fullness or peacefulness we are seeking, so that no one can add to it or take away from it. Not knowing this, we look to our patients for all kinds of things. We avoid what we do not like. We want to create what we like. Liking and disliking have no part in therapy. The third Zen patriarch, Sengstan, put it this way[10] :

The Great Way is not difficult
for those who have no preferences.
When love and hate are both absent
everything becomes clear and undisguised.
Make the smallest distinction, however,
and heaven and earth are set infinitely apart.
If you wish to see the truth

then hold no opinions for or against anything.
To set up what you like against what you dislike
is the disease of the mind.
When the deep meaning of things is not understood
the mind's essential peace is disturbed to no avail.

*   *   *

Much of the literature related to psychotherapy reveals how important consistent empathy is for the recovery of an illness. Heinz Kohut,[11] for example, writes:

> The precariously established self of the child (as revived in the analytic situation) depends for the maintenance of its cohesion on the near perfect empathic responses of the self object.

In describing primitive forms of object relationship in *The Basic Fault*, Michael Balint[12] says:

> If any hitch or disharmony between subject and object occurs, the reaction to it will consist of loud and vehement symptoms suggesting processes of a highly aggressive and destructive or profoundly disintegrated nature, i.e., either as if the whole world, including the self, would have been smashed up or as if the subject would have been flooded with pure and unmitigated aggressive destructive impulses. On the other hand if the harmony is allowed to persist without much disturbance from outside, the reaction amounts to a feeling of tranquil, quiet well-being which is rather inconspicuous and difficult to observe.

The question then is, what is the nature of a mind that can have "near perfect empathic responses of the self object?"

In discussing the environment-patient relationship, many terms are used. Giovachinni talks of primitive mental states with necessary movement to primitive stages of dependence such that the patient can get to know the undifferentiated, unintegrated affectivity they are.[13] M. Masud Khan[14] says what the patient needs is for the therapist to be the protective shield; Kohut speaks of the therapist as the empathic mirror[15]; Margaret Mahler[16] calls it the extra-uterine matrix, Margaret Little[17] the basic unity; D. W. Winnicott speaks of the environment-patient relationship as the holding function of the therapist[18] and the facilitating environment of the therapy.[19] These are often just words. We have terrible trouble and failure putting these valuable words into practice.

A central question for therapists, then, is "How can we gain the kind of abiding mind so that there is consistent empathy with patients who never got this in life and who still suffer from this lack?" How can we truly be free of needing our patients so that they do not have to react to our needs as they did with their parents and can be free to exist and discover who they are?

1.2 Countertransference

Despite our recognition of the need for consistent empathy, the psycho-analytic literature routinely describes the serious difficulty therapists encounter working with patients who are called borderline. Countertrans-ferential dilemmas are taken for granted, and it is their intensity with well-analyzed and even famous therapists that I wish to emphasize. That the nature of these difficulties would obscure the work and create obstacles to the patient's improvement is inevitable. It is assumed that the patient creates turmoil in the mind of the therapist, and not the therapist's own ways of thinking and feeling.

Examples of this sort of thinking abound in the writings of even the most famous psychoanalysts. In his chapter on the general principles of treatment with borderline conditions and pathological narcissism, Dr. Otto Kernberg[20] says:

Chronic countertransference fixations are to an important degree a consequence of the patient's success in destroying the analyst's stable and mature ego identity in their relationship . . . . At the same time, the aggressive behavior of patients with severe transference regression continuously undermines the analyst's self-esteem and self concept in their inter-action, and thus also the integrating ego function of the analyst's ego identity. Thus the analyst may be struggling at the same time with the upsurge of primitive impulses in himself, with the tendency to control the patient as part of his efforts to control these impulses, and with the temptation to submit in a masochistic way to the patient's active efforts of control.

What is the state of mind of the therapist whose ego identity can be "destroyed" by another person? What is the inner condition of an analyst whose self-esteem and self-concept are "continuously undermined"? Surely the analyst here is reacting to the patient and is needing the patient to be another way than the way he is. The patient has to react to the analyst's upsetment and does not have the freedom to exist *as is* in the analysis or the therapy. It is not enough to say that this sort of counter-transference is common. The question is what is the responsibility of the therapist in this situation? Isn't the therapist responsible for his own consciousness and for finding a way to calm it and find what he needs from within himself so that he can, in fact, be free enough of dependency needs to benefit others?

Here is another statement made by an equally famous analyst, Peter Giovachinni, whose sensitivity can be inferred from his clinical reports.

He is one of the leading contributors and most respected people in the work with disturbed non-neurotic patients. Yet in discussing borderline disorders, he says[21]:

Often the therapeutic setting becomes utterly confused. The situation is as devastating to both patient and therapist, but usually the therapist suffers the most.

We often read in the literature that the therapist is "devastated" and "suffers the most." When we experience that the state of our mind is not dependent on external phenomena for our completion, then how can we be continually "devastated" in working with patients, so many of whom are thought to be borderline or narcissistic? Giovachinni further states[22]:

Therapists may find such patients especially irritating and often experience what appears to be a disproportionate amount of frustration. It almost seems that the analyst feels enough frustration for the two of them, that he easily makes up for the patient's inability to feel frustrated, although the patient may feel something much more intense and disruptive.

The most experienced and respected members of our profession describe the reactive mind of the therapist and assume that the therapist must be deeply thrown by working with a disturbed patient.

Others have written about how we will inevitably be transformed by the patient. In *The Fallacy of Understanding*, Edgar Levenson describes an "isomorphic transformation" in which the therapist begins to relate in the same form as the patient. He speaks of the need for the therapist to resist this transformation by being aware of it, but says nothing of when this awareness fails to help.[23] Similarly, Lawrence Epstein writes:

There are some things I want to make clear at this point. I am in full agreement with the view that *all* of the analyst's affective reactions to his patient should be internally treated and neutralized so that they are fully under the control of his ego before any intervention is made. When hate is induced, the patient's interest is safeguarded if the analyst processes his feelings as follows: he should observe the full emotional impact the patient is having on him; be fully aware of counter-destructive impulses and wishes; *reduce the intensity of his feelings without attempting to eliminate them* lest they become dissociated and therefore virulent . . . (Epstein's italics)

As is the case with most psychoanalytic writing on uncontrollable reactions to the patient, it does not *tell us how to "reduce the intensity of feelings,"* but only that this is necessary. How we do this is not discussed by most authors, who simply assume that being aware of them, not rejecting these feelings, is helpful. However, it has been my experience that awareness of countertransference often does not decrease its intensity or frequency when it is blocking the patient's finding out who he is.

The patient cannot connect to many of his feelings if the therapist is having difficulty with countertransference. Although we see the necessity for enabling the patient to experience all the elements of who he is in the therapy, most therapists are not able to allow this freedom, for they are too thrown by some of their own feelings. It is also true that for many therapists, there is considerable difficulty in the realms of hatred confusion, hopelessness, and terror. When the therapist himself cannot tolerate some of the most basic elements of who he is, then he cannot work openly with these elements in the patient. It has been a given in therapy that we all have countertransference responses, but I think we have not been honest in admitting the pervasiveness and seriousness of countertransference, particularly with borderline and narcissistic people. It is now necessary to look at the question of how to begin to resolve it, not just to be aware of it. Epstein[25] goes on to say:

> Why do the destructive tendencies of the patient not enter into the transference neurosis? I would suggest that when such is the case the major reason is that the patient's hate and destructiveness as they emerge in the analysis, beget the analyst's own hate and destructiveness and that for most analysts it is their own hatred more than the patient's that is abhorrent.

I would raise the question as to why we take it for granted in psychotherapy that hate begets hate. We have the responsibility as healers not just to be aware of our hate, but to overcome or reduce it. I would also raise the question as to why analysts hate so much. This is not uncommon for man, and yet with a personal analysis and so much opportunity to see human suffering and more than the usual interest in compassion, why do the analysts and therapists have to much trouble putting this compassion into practice in session? Why is their compassion often qualified? The glib response that we are not perfect avoids confronting the issues of our responsibility for our own minds.

The conclusion of many analysts writing on countertransference is that we have to overcome our self idealization and accept our countertransference. I think it is irresponsible to be working and getting paid to facilitate change when our own consciousness is so dominated by ego needs.

The analytic literature does not usually discuss how to resolve the reactive mind, nor does it speak to the waste this reactivity creates in work in psychotherapy and psychoanalysis. The issue then would be to look not only at the source of the countertransference, the way it helps and hinders, but also to the degree that it hinders our being open to how the patient is, and able to live in this without being thrown. We are then responsible for *overcoming this very countertransference* which blocks the patient from being more whole and from connecting more extensively and intensively with himself. *I think that in looking at how to free ourselves to be more consistently empathic we may have to look outside the psychoanalytic paradigm to see where we can find some guidelines.* For me, helpful direction comes from Eastern spiritual teachings and practices. We shall also have to be more open about how intensely thrown we are by some of our patients, where we form alliances and collusions to maintain the relationship. In many instances our own rage and hopelessness and fear make it impossible to enable the patient to go more deeply into these same phenomena. In too many instances, our awareness of our own feelings does not relieve us, and we are trapped.

How the therapist sees who *he* is in the world, how the therapist answers the question "Who am *I*?" – these will either render him free to allow all the elements in the patient to emerge or will demand that some of them remain blocked, dissociated, out of awareness. Again, to remember M. Masud Khan's words[26]:

The real difference between this analytic experience and other experiences of the patient is that in the analytic experience the patient is able to exteriorize and express *all the facets and elements of his current and developmental experiences* without magically seducing the analyst into collusion or rejection. This ability to be involved without interfering with the patient's inner reality is the most delicate and crucial task.

All the facets of the patient have to be lived out in the therapy and expressed without our rejecting them, without inhibiting them, living with them in full freedom so that the patient can see the actuality of who he is. This goal is very difficult, however, because sometimes patients are nasty, brutal, hateful, uncaring, empty, deadened, confused, terrified, despairing, stuck, sad, hopeless, fragmented. For the therapist to be free of being consistently thrown by the patient in these states, he must experience, over time, the Silence at the source of his own mind, the inner nature of his own fullness, and not be dependent on others for this. Not knowing this we turn to others for satisfaction.

Let us look at just a few typical excerpts from supervision of therapists working with patients who are borderline or narcissistic. In condensed form, some frequent comments I hear in supervision are:

We have no relationship.
Nothing is going on here.
I can't figure out what to do.
If I'm honest, I'd have to say I don't like this patient.
I hear it, but I just don't feel it.
I don't have to take this anymore.

I have the feeling nothing I say makes any difference anyway.
I can't stand what I'm seeing in myself with this patient.

With this kind of auto-analysis or self worry, we can imagine how emotionally available the therapist is in the session, how open. Here are some typical examples of the inner condition of therapists I have supervised.

1.2.1 Examples of countertransference

Example One: The therapist told me that the patient had been talking about quitting. I asked her how she had opened this up. She answered, "I didn't." She continues: "Then, after some nasty cracks she walked out saying she wouldn't be back. I didn't say anything . . . she just left after months of complaining. I saw her 2 years and . . . (crying). I'm tired. I just couldn't stand it anymore. Lots of things are going on in my life. I'm worn out . . . this patient is hammering on me and I feel she's right. I don't know what to do, I didn't help. I knew I couldn't stand how I failed her, and I was waiting for her to go. I can't do it. I get so worn down. I don't have the energy for this. I feel scared of her attacks on me. I hope to hell she'll leave me alone now. I just can't take the beatings week after week. I sit there thinking, 'Get the fuck out and don't bother me anymore. I'm not taking any more patients like this . . . . ' My whole life is trying to do what I don't think I can do. You encouraged me to see the suffering of this patient, but I can only see my own right now. I just went passive. I gave up. I hope she never calls . . . . she won't. I know I can't work with these patients."

Example Two: She attacked me subtly like, "Are you o.k. today? You look tired, etc." She said, "You don't seem to be up for me. You look wiped out," and I smiled. I thought, "If she leaves it's 2 hours. I'm paralyzed by needing the money. But also I m afraid of people quitting . . . . it seems to be a way of realizing I don't know what's happening. I have 18 hours and to be honest I can't pay the rent without this. Frankly, when you talk, sometimes I think you can do all that empathy, inquiry stuff cause you're rich. I can't do it. You're not a man . . . maybe you can't understand what I'm going through."

Example Three: "I have gone over the same stuff with this guy. He doesn't listen to anything I say. I might as well not be in the room. He asks me, he pleads for advice on what to do. I ask questions and he laughs and says I don't do what he asks. I sat in stony silence last week. I said to myself 'I'm finished trying. Let him either work or that's it.' I keep telling him he's not looking at himself and he breaks up laughing. I'm furious. I can feel it even talking about it, but in the room I can hardly control my shaking. I would like to belt him lately. When I point out a defense he says, 'You're cute.' If he doesn't listen . . . then what? What am I doing in there ready to kill him for laughing at me? Therapy is out of the question. For me it's surviving my urge to get up and walk out of the room or to throw him out."

Example Four: The supervisee said, "I told you that his father was kicking him out . . . was fed up. Well, his father packed his stuff and told him he couldn't come back, and that night he came to the session telling me he had no place to go afterwards and I think, 'Where can he go?' Then he asks me to lower the windowshade and I jump up to do it . . . without thinking . . . like I do a lot of stuff, and when I'm by the window he says, 'I can see through your dress . . . you have great tits . . . I like your ass too . . . but your tits are great.' I jumped back to my seat and clenched my hands . . . I am sweating, and he smiles and says, 'I bet a lot of guys say that.' I feel he's made a total fool of me, and we sit till the end of the session. He laughs nervously when the time is up saying, 'I don't know where to go. I don't know if I can go to my sister's house . . . if not I don't know.' I said . . . and I can't believe this . . . I said, 'Our time is up.' I just couldn't do the work anymore. He got up asking if I thought he should go to his sister's, and I just said, 'I don't know.' I walked out of the room before he did. I don't want to see him again. If he comes in I might have to tell him to see someone else."

Example Five: The supervisee is quite anxious and says, "This is hard to say, but I see someone who is so depressed. We don't talk about much, but the patient is in terrible pain, and is deep inside herself. She doesn't want to live, and says that therapy is the last resort. I've talked about her here. She's Barbara. She is so unattractive, and so defeated by all her failures, and she feels so out of things . . . she won't take her medication. She won't go to the day program. I don't see really what there is for her to live for. We both feel the same. I'm thrown by my feeling this way each session. It's been going on in me for months. I don't see any way out for her. She's been this way for about 10 years she says. She just plops herself down for me to do something about, and my attitude is that there isn't anything I can do. My own attitude of hopelessness is getting me down. I am hopeless about her, hopeless about myself as a therapist right now. I know I've wasted 2 years with her."

In these examples we see one therapist after another being thrown by his own dislike of the way the patient is behaving or being. The therapist has little sense of being open any more to finding out how things are, seeing how the patient lives. In fact, each of them is reacting with such dislike that they have stopped being emotionally open and available to the patient's ways of living and being. They have lost the open, empathic attitude of mind and have all been thrown and upset. Each is unable to endure or comfortably bear the weight of the patient's way of being. In each example there is evaluation of the patient's behavior going on. These ways of the therapist's being reactive will prevent the patient from getting to know himself. Each of these therapists is in trouble because they long for therapy to be different, for the person to be different so that they will have more satisfaction and an inner sense of security and worth in their work. The therapist here has forgotten his own source of fullness, his own inner silence, and is filled with likes and dislikes. There is no space here for the patient to exist. Winnicott has said that healthy relating begins in *existing, not reacting.*[27] In this reactive mind environment, the patient cannot exist.

The reactive mind imposes upon others notions, conclusions, theories, ideas, fascinations, revulsions, concepts. We then want something from that other person. I cannot help but want the patient to give me the satisfaction I seek, the fullness I seek. Not knowing that I already have it all the time in myself, I think I have to gain this from patients. So then I create a particular set-up in treatment to give me satisfaction. Often I do not know I am creating this collusion. I like a particular way of working that does not upset me. I create this, I form an alliance to be comfortable. I want to protect myself from seeing my primitive rage, hurt, fear, sorrow. I react with disquiet when patients do not like me, when I do not like what they do, when they do not get better, when they do not believe what my notions say is correct, etc. My mind gets torn up into concepts when things are not going to my liking or according to my notions of how they should go. I separate myself from the patient further and create conditions that further isolate creature from creature, leading to more disturbance. I do this because of the way I was taught to think something is good or bad, right or wrong. I do this as I am dependent on an external object for my sense of completion.

One day I may realize that little anger, disappointment, etc., is expressed. I see that the patient has learned to react to my needs. Then I ask, "What am I doing with this person so that there is little depth of feeling . . . am I keeping things the way I need them, I like them, to feel secure? Have I re-conditioned the patient to meet another set of needs in order to gain some warmth, some comfort? Then I am creating some external system of ways you have to be that made the patient sick in the first place, when he was not allowed to be himself. Being aware of this, I see the necessity for transforming my own consciousness first if I am to help others.

The inner work of the therapist then is first to see the way that the reactive mind limits the work and then find ways to lessen the reactive mind. *Reactivity in the therapist's mind is the great obstacle in therapy and makes healing impossible.* We create the patient out of our mind. Heisenberg's Principle shows that we cannot separate the patient from our thoughts because both create the interpersonal situation. The degree to which we create what we see outside our head is described in quantum theory, where the electron has no objective properties outside of our own mind. The patient has no objective properties independent of my mind. I must put this mind in order so that it can remain open to what I hear and see.

Only when we are free from likes and dislikes can we create another person, called patient, who is more whole. The question is how to reach that state of freedom. My observation and experience suggests that traditional western psychotherapy, with its analysis of the therapist and reliance on the rational, is often insufficient for consistently sustaining the disposition of mind that heals.

When you have experienced your mind in meditation many times, you see that what you want is simply to be with yourself as you are. In meditation, in silence without a wish for gain, we see the end of the wanting mind, and when we just sit and crave nothing, we find the state of mind where we are complete. When we meditate, we are with ourselves as we are, everything that happens is of equal value and we simply see it and let it go. There is no evaluation of this being with ourselves. Whatever it is is *the way*, is perfect as it is. We then see that it is not an external object that creates our happiness but rather, it is a state of mind that creates what we seek.

This knowledge reduces the craving of the mind for finding pleasure, security, meaning from patients. In this state of not needing, the mind will gain objectivity and will not be so reactive to patients. As therapists, we must see the destructive power of the reactive mind and see and experience the intensity of its tyranny over us. It is these reactive thoughts and feelings that keep us from being empathic with our patients.

1.2.2 An Example of Dualism

A supervisee told me that she had run into a friend that day on the street. The friend looked tired, and told her that she was having a hard time in her life, was beginning to question the work she was doing, felt she couldn't leave it because of the money, was worried and was having trouble sleeping. The supervisee said that she had spontaneously felt her friend's inner pain and said something of how hard this all was, and she was sorry she was going through this. They had talked it over a little and arranged to have dinner.

The supervisee said, "How different this was for me than being with a patient where I might have worried about what I was going to say, thinking I might have said the wrong thing, feeling I didn't do enough. Another difference was that with my friend I was feeling, and with a lot of patients, I don't know why, that doesn't happen for me. I guess 'cause I have so many ideas about therapy and how it should go, and in life it just goes and I go with it.

This separation of therapy from life is common. This separation of therapist from patient is common. Theory gives us the basis for ways to understand and interpret, but when we are with the patient we *are* the theory and cannot let concepts interfere with what we perceive and hear. Deviations from theoretical concepts set up reactions. At this point we have lost empathy and are out to prove something in the work. The Zen student is told by the teacher, "Be the rain." When we are totally absorbed in rain, we can be it in that the self disappears in listening. In the same way we gain empathy when we can be the patient without concepts to separate us. We then experience what the patient is going through and telling us. We then know where the patient is coming from inside and we do understand this person deeply from our experience of him.

Fire burns. I have to learn to deal with fire as it is. I do not like it or dislike it. There is no problem in this. We have to learn to live with patients as they are. As long as there are likes and dislikes this is not possible. *In reaction I want things to be a particular way. The thing as it is disquiets me. The problem is created by my likes and dislikes. Sorrow comes from longing for things to be different than they are.*

The nature of experience of the "I" which enables us to know who we are so that we are not disquieted is described in this Hindu meditation:

Awareness IS
   and it is . . . Free . . .
   It lacks nothing, is bound by nothing.
   Time doesn't touch it, space doesn't enclose it.

*   *   *

Awareness . . . is free.
   Is ever free.
   I AM free . . . for
   Awareness is I.

*   *   *

I think of an object . . .
   I'm free to think of . . .
   and it is in Awareness . . .
   it is in me.

*   *   *

I dismiss the object.
   I am free.
I am Free . . .
Free . . . Is myself
I need no freedom . . .
   I AM freedom
I seek no freedom . . .
   I Am freedom

*   *   *

This level of Self where I am what I seek is always there . . . it is the state of mind that I always sought in externals. It is this knowledge that frees me from having to seek from my patients but allows me to do my work with a sense of appreciation for what is taking place with my patients.

1.3 Ending the Reactive Mind

To know that we are the fullness that we seek is to end the reactive mind. Knowing this "I" as who *I am*, through spiritual practice and experience, is freeing me from the illusion that what I want is different than what I am.

When I come to know that the deepest level of self is the same for all of us, that we are forms in the unlimited awareness of the universe, then duality dissolves and I am aware that at the deepest level all people are the same. Experiencing this again and again, we no longer feel so separate from others; being empty of concepts at the deepest level, being goodness at the deepest level, we connect with people in a faith and commonality that is empathic.

When I am calm and aware of my own fullness within, I live in a way where another person cannot throw me around inwardly. This is the disposition of mind that heals. In this inner condition I give the patient the freedom to find the Silence Awareness that is the beginning of ending of sorrow and hatred and fear. I have faith that with my knowing through experience that I am whole, that this can happen to another person working with me. Whatever presence I put forth, whatever being or spirit I embody, will be felt by the patient and will make a difference in his life.

Emptiness which is all full is the essence of any person as water is the essence of the wave. Knowing this I do not need from patients.

Can we heal another person without intimately knowing the whole of who we are such that we are not dependent on others for our completion Can we be consistently empathic without a knowledge of this level of the self? I do not think it is possible. I would say that before intimately and consistently knowing this level of self, the self that is Silence Awareness, we will have the troubles described in the analytic literature in enabling others to get to know the whole of who they are.

There is often a natural move from psychologically getting to know the individual "I" to getting to know the level of "I" which is universal, which we all share. There is a natural link between the psychological and the spiritual.

Having this knowledge of the self which is always full and whole, the healer is no longer so thrown by life's events, is not so reactive, can move openly with what comes up, knowing the whole of who he is. This knowledge of the nature of who am "I" of the holistic therapist has freed him to be the fullness he is. He can now let others be fully and freely who they are, *knowing that at the deepest level we are all one awareness* out of which various and unique forms arise. It is as though with our intrinsic happy nature we are the Ocean and we have the illusion that we are a bucket of water. When I need nothing to be full from Others . . . I am not threatened. This is the mind that one could call the "facilitating environment."

I am the fullness that I seek. Knowing this fullness intimately through repeated experience is the disposition of mind that heals. I discover this fullness by experiencing my own mind in Silence in therapy and further in the spiritual practice of meditation. Out of this Silence, the source of all thought and feeling, true unqualified compassion can emerge.

The disposition of mind that can heal intimately knows the level of mind where there is Silence Awareness, where there is emptiness, where there is fullness without seeking. This lessens our dependence on patients. The therapist disposed to heal sees the dangers of the reactive mind. There is also an awareness of how our notions of ourselves and others keep us from being open and seeing people as they are. It is not then a situation of being aware of our countertransference with patients. It is not enough to accept our reactions and countertransference and know that they teach us who the patient is. Our negative reactions block the patient's healing when they continue. We have to now expand our inner experience of our own mind beyond ego to the Silence source of mind within so that we can truly give people the consistent empathy and freedom they need to heal.

References

1. M. Masud R. Khan, "Clinical Aspects of the Schizoid Personality: Affects and technique," *The Privacy of the Self* (New York: International Universities Press, Inc.) 1974. pp. 24–25.
2. Edward Conze, *Buddhist Meditation* (New York: Harper & Row, Harper Colophon Books, 1975) pp. 17-18.
3. Meditations from the Vedanta class of Sandra Eisenstein, New York.
4. Swami Dayananda Saraswate and Sandra Eisenstein, "Discerning the Fundamental Problem according to Advaita Vedanta," in *Studies in Non-Deterministic Psychology*, edited by Gerald Epstein, M. D. (New York: Human Sciences Press, 1980) p. 48.
5. Lao Tzu, *Truth and Nature*, trans. Cheng Lin (Taiwan: World Book Company Ltd., 1969) p. 25.
6. *Ibid.*, p. 31.
7. R. H. Blyth, "The Hsinhsinming," in *Zen and Zen Classics*, Vol. One (The Hokuseido Press, 1960) p. 83.
8. *Ibid.*, p. 87

9. Lao Tzu, *The Way of Life*, trans. Witter Bynner (New York: Capricorn Books, 1962) verse 57.

10. Sengstan, *Verses on the Faith Mind*. Translation of Hsinhsinming (Sharon Springs, N. Y.: Zen Center, 1976).

11. Heinz Kohut, *The Restoration of the Self.* (New York: International Universities Press) p. 91.

12. Michael Balint, *The Basic Fault* (Tavistock Publications, 1968) p. 70.

13. Peter Giovachinni, *Treatment of Primitive Mental States* (Jason Aronson, 1979).

14. M. Masud Khan, *op. cit.*, p. 44.

15. Heinz Kohut, *The Analysis of the Self.* New York: International Universities Press, 1971.

16. Margaret Mahler, "On Human Symbiosis and the Vicissitudes of Individuation," *Journal of the American Psychoanalytic Association*, Vol. 15, 740–763, 1967.

17. Margaret Little, "The Analyst's Total Response to His Patient's Needs," *International Journal of Psychoanalysis*, Vol. 38, 1957.

18. D. W. Winnicott, "The Theory of the Parent Infant Relationship," *The Maturational Processes and the Facilitating Environment* (New York: International Universities Press, 1965) p. 43.

19. D. W. Winnicott, *op. cit.* "A Theory of Psychiatric Disorder," p. 239.

20. Otto Kernberg, *Borderline Conditions and Pathological Narcissism* (New York: Jason Aronson, Inc.) p. 88.

21. Peter Giovachinni, *op. cit.*, p. 145.

22. *Ibid.*, p. 145.

23. Edgar Levenson, *The Fallacy of Understanding* (New York: Basic Books Inc.) p. 41.

24. Lawrence Epstein, "The Therapeutic Function of Hate." *Countertransference*, edited by Lawrence Epstein and Arthur Feiner (New York: Jason Aronson Inc., 1979) p. 228.

25. *Ibid.*, p. 218.

26. M. Masud Khan *op. cit.*,

27. D. W. Winnicott, *op. cit.* "Ego Distortion in Terms of True and False Self, p. 148.

V. Healing in Psychotherapy: The Process of Holistic Change

How do we know when the therapeutic event reflects holistic change? At such moments of changing we observe a greater energy, a person becoming more at ease with himself, less self-consciousness, less preoccupation with compulsive thoughts and feelings. Awareness of who one is becomes more complete, feelings are more genuinely expressed, thoughts open to include new connections. In holistic change the participants experience new connections in the form of new thoughts, feelings, sensations, images, dreams, fantasies. There is a letting go into silence, a forgetting of self-consciousness or intellectual notions to where one is being oneself, forgetting to be governed by an idea of who one should be. Such moments of participation give increased strength to the individual for he learns that he is not only his thoughts or his feelings but is something more . . . something that is always his, such that he never forgets that he is. This ever-present awareness leads to seeing that we are not exclusively our thoughts, we are not our bodies, we are not our feelings, since we can witness our bodies, our feelings, our thoughts. There is in us a witnesser, the "I" that always remains. Knowing this, we are then not so thrown around by the body, thoughts, feelings. They go on but they do not control "me" any more. In healing, a person becomes aware that there is a larger whole that always remains. We call it awareness, and this awareness is the source of healing.

As a holistic healing event, therapy discards one veil of ignorance after another. As we facilitate patients' opening to us, we see that what people lose in therapy are their facades, pretenses. People lose their ignorance of who they are. To be aware of what is happening in the moment, open to the effects of one's action, is to transcend fixed ideas, to let go of past notions of who we are, to be ourselves, to forget ourselves, and thus to be whole.

To live in the moment is to live wholeheartedly *in* what is taking place, being who we are, our nature unfolding as we are aware of creating our life moment by moment.

The point to be emphasized in healing in psychotherapy is the therapist's strong confidence in and consistent awareness of our original nature, knowing that we will come to know it in the therapeutic relationship and work. This means that therapy as a healing event is less a learning process than an unlearning process. In practicing it we strive to relinquish those things that the world has taught us that make us compulsive and rigid. Therapy is a process of loss and gain in which we continually shed old ideas of how life should go for us. We shed those belief systems that protect us from being open to the moment.

In therapy we see in our long-term work that people are always seeking their original nature, which is full and open . . . they will move to it when the therapist provides the freedom for them to be who they are.

To be alive is to participate in movement and change. The therapist is a person who hears and sees the movement and change taking place inside the patient, in the therapeutic relationship, inside himself in interaction with the patient, and in the patient's way of being with others, his ways of living in the world, living in the session.

Healing is not a re-arrangement, a fixing of the patient, but a respect for the healing function of the patient's finding for himself the facts of who he truly is. The therapist works to facilitate the patient's revealing more and more of his actuality. What creates fragmentation is the avoidance of discovering actuality. What facilitates wholeness is seeing what is, being what is.

The therapist knows the profound meaning of human relating which is, as Lao Tzu said, "beyond the power of words to define." [1] He sees the wonder of someone wanting to find his true nature, his quest for it, the wonder of his finding it. At one time in our lives we have *known* what we are searching for, otherwise we would not be searching for it . . . for we would be ignorant that it exists. We have known the happiness we seek, otherwise we could not long for it . . . and the wonder is that we do want to know the truth of ourselves. The realization of the fact that we were and are what we are seeking . . . having been it, having lost it . . . stays with the healer and allows him to be patient, to have compassion for the ways our nature got twisted. He has faith that in an open, non-evaluative environment, people will gain the knowledge they seek, the fullness they seek, for they have the means to attain it. The therapist changes the perspective of the patient from a wish to be certain ways he was trained to think were good, to a wish to find out who he is in fact, and to see then that who he is is good, is enough, to live within his place in the scheme of things. The patient is out to prove himself . . . the therapist sees that there is nothing to prove, that being who we are as is is enough. The healing function of therapy includes the discovery that life is uncertain once we go beyond our own actions. We cannot control life's events.

The terror of the patient in being with himself can be healed only in a human relationship. D. W. Winnicott has stated that we learn to be with ourselves by being with others first.[2] As we see that another will give us the freedom to be who we are in fact, we relax, we begin to discover the incipient processes within. We begin to trust, our pain is felt more deeply, our joys more deeply. We see that the pain is self-created by our fixed thoughts such that the end of pain lies in our letting it be, then the dropping away which occurs after we live in it. Psychological pain is caused b avoidance. *Participation in what is* creates healing.

A question to be asked is, what is the disease from which the patie suffering? All patients, as I see it, are basically suffering from not able to be who they are. They suffer the sorrow of fictitious Patients still live life on the basis of how mother and father demandeu they be. They have lost touch with who they are in fact, that self that is intrinsically whole emanating from within.

Healing occurs at those moments when the patient discovers what is his personal own: his thoughts, feelings, images, sensations, fantasies, dreams. The patient is deeply conditioned to be the way he was seen by others. Often no one has been interested in or really cared about how the patient felt, what he thought, what his subjective experiences were. This past conditioning does not encourage him to know what he personally thinks, feels, sees. As the patient is given the freedom to be himself, encouraged to inquire, he moves out of his compulsive ways of living and thinking, and healing takes place.

*   *   *

Now I want to discuss some specific moments when healing that moves towards holistic change occurs in psychotherapy with all types of patients.

1.1 Healing Occurs in the Moment of the New . . . Outside the Conditioned and Compulsive

We as therapists recognize what is new — when the patient stretches out beyond the confines of his past, what is outside the usual compulsive behavior — and explore it. Pathology is that which is fixed, formed, compulsive, cannot be changed out of fear. These habitual patterns of behavior close off life's possibilities. In discovering new things inside and outside oneself, healing occurs. These include new images of self, others, world, new interests, responses, sensations, etc. Here are *events that are beginning to take place.*

1.1.1   An Example of healing in the moment of the new

A patient had always gone to her class right before it met to avoid socializing. She casually described getting there early and sitting with others. I heard this as new and explored her experience with this. The patient denied its meaning. I emphasized her ability to be with others, her anxiety, living in it, as new assets. I asked why she wanted to do this. She laid it to accident. I inquired about what else went into it, and she laughed. We both laughed.

Here was another *moment in the new* which we mutually shared. In this moment of participating in the new together, healing occurred. We had never laughed with understanding on this level of mutual respect before. We both appreciated the patient's movement and her way with this, which was to deny . . . she laughed at her own way, which meant she not only saw it, but also shared it with me. Here we see a second form that healing takes in therapy.

1.2   Healing occurs in the action of participating experientially in the session

Patients feel they do not create their own fate. They are influenced by others to do as they are told, live out other people's images of who they should be. They do not feel they create their own life as they go along, free to participate in what is taking place. They talk *about* themselves, waiting for the therapist to make it better, or see life acting on them.

However, as a person is guided by the therapist's open-ended questions and interests to go into the specifics of an event, he begins to *participate in the telling* so that there is a shedding of self-consciousness, a shedding of the idea of how things should go, a shedding of doubts, conflicts, images of how he should think and feel to where there is engagement, the *action of participation* in the telling.

In this action of participation, the patient has *an emotional experience* of his own. He does not imitate or act dissociated from feelings. This emotional experiencing may focus on his thoughts, feelings, description, images, or on his interaction with the therapist.

1.3   Whenever a Person has an Emotional Experience that is Authentically His Own, Healing Occurs

At such moments of experiencing, the patient is feeling and thinking beyond his usual conditioned patterns and is being more whole. By exploring more of the specifics of an internal or external event, the therapist elicits and deepens experiencing. Once having something of his own in the way of a personal, unconditioned experience, the patient is more whole.

1.3.1 An Example of an emotional experience that is authentically a Person' own

A flat, non-talkative, detached man was sent by his parents to session. He was sure only that his parents wanted him to come in order to get a job. He'd lost several jobs. He had little idea what he wanted to do. He was dull, listless, and responded only when spoken to.

One day he mentioned degrading himself – that he was "a janitor in his family, cleaned the basement." I asked what there was to clean. He tossed it off, said he was "kidding." I asked him what he did in the basement, and he said, "I practically live there." Again I asked exactly what he did there and he said, "I muse at my desk."

I asked specific questions about where he got the desk, what it was made of, what led him to get it, what was in the drawers, what he did at the desk. As he told me of his purchase, his caring for the desk, his refinishing it, his whole manner changed to *active participation*. I asked what he did at the desk and he laughed, saying, "I mostly daydream, but I also write poems." I found this out for the first time. My participation in this moment of healing was to feel his enthusiasm, to explore the particularities of his basement, his creativity, his work, his dreams, his desk, his actual efforts in life, where he was in fact alive and natural.

I participated in this healing event by appreciating its significance to the patient and to me. Recognizing his *action of participation* as it took place in the session, I had a new, more hopeful image of the patient. I responded to him differently. In turn he was more whole in this session as he formed new connections to his habitual thought fragment, "I can't do anything to make my life better."

After this session the patient was more energetic. Having shared a secret (writing poems), he felt closer to me, felt stronger for having taken a chance, and saw that I cared about what he was saying.

Our work is finding ways to facilitate *the patient's participation in new forms of living in the session.*

We *watch* for these moments and participate in them by joining the patient as they occur through exploration related to them, or through recognition and appreciation that they occur. To point out such moments of participation as they occur is contraindicated. At moments of participation the therapist moves with the patient by encouraging opening out of the event through questions, reflection, or silence. Here we give the patient the space to own his new ways of being, and do not interrupt the process of fuller affective participation with interpretations.

There are levels of intensity with which experiencing occurs. At moments when you forget yourself, you become one with your experience and your action. These are intensely felt moments of healing. A good session therefore is one in which the patient and therapist are engaged, everything is just as it is, what comes up is experienced and is felt as valid — there is no judgment or evaluation of what is taking place. These are the moments of healing which will serve as touchstones for what it is to be in relating, to be finding the self, forgetting the self in immersion in the moment. Having such moments, one knows life in a new way. One knows life as sufficient as is.

It is the function of the therapist to facilitate such experiencing and then to participate by letting the patient be and not interrupting the experiencing when it is taking place for the patient.

1.4 Healing Occurs as the Patient Sees the Actuality of Who He Is

It occurs as the patient experiences the facts of who he is, how he lives, and lets himself be who he is. As the patient sees himself *as is*, he feels more sound, more healthy, even though what he sees may be painful, may create suffering. In experiencing actuality, patients learn to bear pain, they learn that pain passes once they can experience it. Then they develop respect for whatever is coming up in them.

1.4.1 Examples of the patient seeing the actuality of who he is

Example One: A patient has been talking for months of driving herself to fulfill her image of who she should be. She can't stop doing countless things. She is panicked, frantic, exhausted. Still she drives herself.

One day, she says with feeling, "I'm tired." I say nothing, giving her space to feel this. She begins to cry. She is seeing herself in fact, the way she lives in fact, not wanting to do most of what she does. She spends several moments deeply sobbing. At this moment of seeing clearly the actuality of her fatigue, she feels some beginning compassion for herself, for her lack of freedom to be herself, not her image, for her being who she is: tired, driven.

Example Two: A woman describes her boss as being unintelligent, unfair, judgmental. Each time she has dealings with him, she is furious, disappointed. I point out to her that she has told me repeatedly how he is limited, unknowing. How come she keeps longing for him to be another person than the person he is *in fact*?

The patient is silent. She says, "He is stupid. Why can't I accept that? I keep hoping he'll be different . . . " The patient then says angrily, "I can't learn from him . . . it means really I have to do it on my own or quit . . . I see how dumb he is . . . it's amazing how I've been fighting this for 3 years . . . I have to do something."

Th: What?

Pt: To stop hoping . . . who knows? But now I see I'll have to do something.

Th: Maybe to stop longing for it to be different?
Pt: Longing . . . always. Just to see he's not able to teach me. That's incredible. I feel I can finally stop wishing it was different.

What is there in *seeing oneself or the world as is, in actuality,* that enables the patient to be more sound, more whole? First, after seeing the way things are in fact, the patient can stop longing for things to be different. Second, at the moment the patient sees who he is in fact, he is living his own way, is being himself, which is whole and complete as is. It is only our thoughts that tell us what we are is not enough, not complete. Our fixed ideas of how things should go take us away from our actuality and create conflict.

The experience of the *actual* has the effect of ending the patient's strain of trying to be another way than the way he is in fact. It reduces the separation between the patient's thoughts and his experience. It creates a new sense of internal balance, ease, substance, and this is healing.

Example Three: A patient tells me she is scared to begin her job, adding, "I don't want it to show, but I feel good knowing it; I can feel what it would be to pretend I wasn't. So be it, and then . . . "
Th: Then?
Pt: (laughing) Either I'll get fired or I won't . . . I can't tell you how good it is to see that it isn't crazy to be scared. I mean other people are scared, too. So . . . I'll see. I'll have to see.
Th: I know, but tell me . . .
Pt: I feel so like smiling. I'm scared and glad to know it. That's really crazy.

Here the patient experiences intensely many feelings, all her own: being scared, glad to know her feelings. However, it is important to note that as the patient discovers the facts *as is,* she doesn't feel so isolated from her fellow humans. She sees that she has commonalities with others, and this connects her to other people. This creates a new internal soundness. The patient is creating new wholeness or healing as she and the therapist clarify the actuality.

The act of seeing what is creates a new situation in life, a new way to live that lets in new possibilities.

1.5 Whenever two people participate openly together, aware of the present moment they share, there is healing

Out of such participation, both people have more inner sense of energy.

All patients have difficulty living with another person in the moment as the event moves into uncertainty, open to what comes up. The terror in relating for us all is based on the clear openness between us. Can you let in the way a person feels . . . simply let it in . . . not think "Can I make it better?" Then you are being more whole as a therapist. Can you see the person as is without concepts . . . only then can you see the person. The patient more often participates with the image of the therapist made up in his head, participating with his own talk, obliterating the therapist's existence in many ways so that mutuality is not experienced. The patient turns himself into a passive object to be done to by the therapist so there is little open sharing together in the moment as it is being created. Thus the patient often feels radically separated from the therapist. The patient works to prove that he needs or doesn't need help. He talks *in order* to be fixed, changed, helped, not in order to discover mutually with another who he is or simply to be with others. With patients, we often feel the patient is talking to himself, about himself, that he is not talking to us as another person in the spirit of mutuality. The moment of healing occurs when there is movement outside of the roles of patient/therapist, when there is a sharing where the roles end, thought ends, and people are letting go of images and truly being who they are together. Real change is being in the not-having-to-be state.

The patient does not know that help exists in the world, that in the world there is real support for human suffering. The patient has often never been with another, significant person without having made plans, without knowing something of what would happen, without "things" to discuss. The patient has usually never experienced the mutual process of co-operating together to arrive at some understanding where no one for certain was "right," where people came together in order to find out, not to proselytize. The patient has little experience of another person's simply wanting to be with him for no particular reason. Restated then, the terror of the patient is in simply being with another person *as is* without images of how it should go, agendas, activities, etc. The clear openness between two people being who they are, experiencing one another *as is*, is fraught with fear and thus is avoided. When a patient moves from a focus on accomplishing or doing to simply being present in awareness of the moment, engaging what comes up, there is a big inner transformation.

As therapists, we often close the gap with talk, the need to help, the need to know, theory, ideas, control, memories of other patients, conclusions, formulation of diagnoses, themes. At the moment of mutual participation in the moment, however, what is remains complete as it is. There is no desire for anything else. There is experience without concepts. There is a fullness which we find in sharing together in creating the moment with the patient. There is an appreciation of this being together in the moment, needing nothing more than this to happen . . . being together is sufficient. This experience of mutual closeness often is missing in earlier life before therapy.

In holistic therapy one wants to see how human beings relate, to know who the patient is and how he lives in the world. His acts, his behavior are not met with reactions that want things to be different than they are. It is the way of the individual that is of interest to us. In therapy we do not know; we pay attention to find out. In such moments of participating together, thoughts of therapist/patient drop away. Thoughts of having to do and to fix drop away.

1.5.1 Example of therapist/patient participating together

Example One: A 32-year-old transvestite often described eating dinner with his mother at a table in the living room. The room was dim, night coming on. His mother, divorced, often came home from work tired. She cooked. They ate, talking of the day's events.

Pt: Then there was a terrible silence. I couldn't look at my mother. I would jump up from the table when it got quiet. I would look at my stamps, clear the dishes, homework, anything. *I couldn't just be with her.* I would go upstairs to my grandma's 'cause she had TV. I don't know . . .

Th: What would you see being with your mother?

Pt: (breaking into sobs) She was so sad. I couldn't stand it. She was so lonely. And there wasn't anything I could do. I couldn't go with her even for a walk when she got sad. I would go off into fantasy.

I'm afraid still to just be with her without doing something. I don't want to come to her sadness. (crying)

I remember once I was with her. We had a great time buying stamps and then as we got to the house the sadness began . . . and I went into my aunt's drawer and put on the tightest corset I could find. I wanted to strangle the feeling of loving my mom, of hating her sadness. I tightened and tightened and then I felt the relief of not feeling. . . . Just to be with another person. I'm still afraid they'll be sad or lonely . . . (silence) . . . of my own sadness . . . or of yours (crying).

And once I saw your face being sad and I began to hum a song . . . to not be with you, to feel you . . . or myself . . .

There's so much sadness in me . . . in you. (silence) I wanted to cry with my mother, now with you . . . (cries)

(Patient cries for minutes . . . then relaxes and is silent a moment. He looks at me and relaxes, beginning to smile.)

At least I'm here . . . not taking myself out of it now.

Example Two: Pt: I never was just with my father. It was always what did I do, homework, chores, what didn't I do . . . In the car with him coming home from Sunday school, if there was no talking I was scared. I was scared to death just to be with him. . . . I don't know why.

And I was that way with you. I was sure you wanted me to be more interesting. I still think so, but it's okay to be with you, and not talk. I don't know why.

I can just be with you and not have to accomplish. God . . . (sigh) . . . (patient closes eyes) . . . I don't understand anything . . . I feel very glad to be with you and ashamed, and . . . (silence) . . . glad. I feel peaceful being here. It's so great not to have to accomplish . . . I just had this thought that you like to be with me too . . . I want to let this in . . . .

Example Three: Pt: Could you talk?

Th: Sure.

Pt: Could you not talk?

Th: (silent)

Pt: (silent) This is weird. I feel you. It scares me to death. I feel me. Talk.

Th: Okay.

Pt: Let's just be together and not talk a minute.

Th: (silent)

Pt: (laughing, more relaxed) . . . You are really nuts. You know that . . .

Th: (laughing)

Pt: You know why I come here? I don't.

Th: Well, let's not figure it out.

Pt: You *are* something. *We* are something, aren't we. (patient begins to flush, is silent for minutes – patient and therapist are in deep contact in sharing the moment)

Example Four: A patient, 33, a psychologist who is afraid to cross the street alone, afraid to be in close relationship with people for very long, after 2 years of treatment:

Pt: (silent, looks at therapist from couch) This is it, right? . . . what it's about . . .

Th: (feeling a deep caring for patient . . . says nothing)
    (There is a mutual looking at one another for seconds; then there are minutes of silence)

Pt: I care about you. I never felt this way. I thought I was so feeling.

Th: (silent)

Pt: There's nothing to say . . . (silence) . . . Well, maybe I can change.

Th: Maybe . . . you can. (smiling)

Pt: Ha, ha. You know I am. You're not so much better than me, you know. Christ . . . (silence) . . . If I thought it was the two of us together that helped . . . I'd collapse.

Th: Collapse now then.

Pt: (very seriously) What is there? This moment now? . . . (looking at therapist)

Th: (looking at patient)
    (There is mutual silence, a being together being ourselves)

Following this session, patient states she feels "totally different . . . more real, less tense." Therapist senses this in herself, too. Patient meets a man 2 weeks after this session with whom she subsequently has a close and long relationship.

1.6 Healing occurs as fragmentation is reduced

As new connections are laid down, the person sees more of the whole of how things are. He is identified less with the compulsive fragments by which he has defined himself. The laying down of the new connections is the being more whole, the seeing new aspects of the whole of all of his qualities as a person.

1.6.1 Example of healing occuring as fragmentation is reduced

Pt: I had no friends . . .
Th: Not the tiniest friendship?
Pt: Not a real friendship.
Th: What's a real friendship?
Pt: When two people care about each other.
Th: Did you ever care for someone?
Pt: I cared but they didn't.
Th: Who most?
Pt: Most? I liked this guy in grade school. He was a big shot . . . we knew each other and then he went to camp and it was over. He came back with new friends.
Th: What about before camp?
Pt: What about?
Th: Were you friendly before camp?
Pt: That's what made it so lousy. We had fun playing . . . I had fun and then still he was only with me 'cause this other guy he liked lived far away.
Th: Fun playing what?
Pt: Stickball . . .
Therapist asks some questions about the stickball playing. Patient speaks of two other boys who played and how camp came up and his friend went with other kids . . . I ask about the other 2 boys, who were they. One lived in his building, he saw him frequently, fought with him, etc.

Here the patient is filling in, finding more contact with who he is, how he lived. His former definition of himself, "I had no friends," has expanded to where more wholeness is included in his perceptions. More of the whole of the reality comes into awareness as the therapist facilitates the patient's opening up the thoughts which had previously been constricted and repetitive.

Illness is fragmentation. A person is more whole as we open out the fragment by going into particularities, find out the actuality of what took place, for there is *more* of him, he is more substantial, less fragile, less torn from the whole complexity of his actual life. He defines himself less and less by just a few thoughts, feelings, images.

1.7 Healing Occurs as the Therapist Recognizes the Transformation to More Wholeness

As the patient participates with more involvement, more of his whole being, discovers more who he is, more how he lives . . . at those moments the therapist *sees* and *appreciates* these healing events. It is in the therapist's action of recognition, appreciation, that empathic mirroring which Heinz Kohut says is necessary for healthy development, takes place. The patient is *seen* as more whole, more of who he is: thus he is sounder. The image of the patient changes for the therapist.

Once the therapist *sees* movement in the patient, there is a new system with a new momentum with faith that it will continue to unfold, not without knots, but with a straighter thread, fewer distortions. As we see a patient as more whole, we treat him differently. "We are as others regard us," Harry Stack Sullivan said.[3] We are the reflected appraisals of others. Because the therapist's attitude is different, the patient feels different about himself.

1.8 Holistic Change Occurs When We Let the Patient Be Who He is Without Evaluation, Which is Experiencing Without Concepts

Healing occurs within the context of the right disposition of mind in the therapist. This mind wants to see the world as it is in fact. This mind values seeing things as they are without likes or dislikes, without evaluation.

In healing we move from the abstraction of talking about, theorizing, to the concrete participation in the moment as it is taking place.

When we are able to free the mind of concepts, we can see clearly without preconceived notions. The patient then feels that it is safe to be himself and the therapist's clarity of perception allows the patient's needs to be observed accurately. The talent of the therapist is to know where the patient is coming from behind the screen of words, by observing fully. In the following example, the patient did not talk, but what I observed was her growing relaxation and greater comfort with me. She also kept coming to sessions. Because of this observable attitude on her part, I decided not to hospitalize her but simply to go on and watch what occurred as we went along. I made no reference to her having a problem nor made any suggestion that there was something wrong with her not talking.

1.81 Example of letting the patient be by observing

The patient is referred to me by a college counselling service. Patient has been missing classes, has revealed that she once heard someone in her bedroom who wasn't there. Patient is given tranquillizers by her physician. In my office the patient is frightened. She says that she cannot tell me what is bothering her because it is too scary, but that last night she banged her head against the wall . . . patient falls into silence. The above was stated in a near whisper.

Patient is asked if she feels she is needing to be in the hospital. Patient says, "Oh no. My brother was crazy." Patient is asked if she feels she is going crazy and says "No." There is more frozen silence. Patient is asked if she would rather come to see me every day for a while until she feels more relaxed. She says yes, and we arrange this for 1 week.

She falls into another silence. I ask her what she is experiencing now, and she looks at the floor. I say that it is okay not to talk now, that I can see that she would like to be quiet. Would she like me to say anything in particular? She then asks if I think she is crazy. I say that I don't think so but that she might be having scary things happening that might upset her. She nods her head. I ask if this is so. She nods.

She comes every day for 1 week. I talk casually and make very few comments about her appearing to be a bit more relaxed. After that, we cut back to 2 times a week.

The patient then begins to return to class. She requests tranquillizers. She does not talk much in the session. She appears quite sad. She says once during the next month that she is flunking chemistry. She does flunk. She has to go to summer school.

During the next 3 months she comes once a week and sits on the edge of the couch. I ask her most times if she wants to say anything. For 3 months she does little more than shake her head. She does not look at me but stares at the wall or at the floor as I talk or don't talk. I feel she is more relaxed over time. She occasionally looks at me.

One day she reports that she has passed chemistry with a B and will return to school in the fall. She whispers. During this time I ask her if there is anything she wants to have happen in the time we spent together. She says, "You talk." I ask if there is anything in particular she would like to say, and she says "No."

I then talk about going to school, Spanish (a subject she took), silence, talking and what people think of it, what I think some of her interests might be, i.e., religion and ballet. She smiles for the first time in 3 months and says, "How did you know?" I say it was based on her wearing a cross and my intuition.

I then speak of how I used to dance and a few of the things I thought about certain religious ideas and practices. At times I am silent, and she sneaks a look at me but does not speak. At times I ask if it is different for her here now, if she feels a bit easier with me, but receive no answers. I watch her face and note that after this time she is more responsive to what I say.

I then say that from what I see, I think she is ready to talk a bit more. She says, "No." I say, "Okay, but I have to trust my hunches. I think it's okay for you to tell me a few things about yourself."

I ask her some questions and she begins to answer. The talk in sessions is quite sparse, but the mood is more relaxed. Occasionally she comes in and says, "You talk today." I laughed and said that she sounded like a little girl who wanted to take charge of what happened to her . . . and she began to cry. She cried for a few minutes and said, "Please talk to me." I asked her what the tears might say to me and she said, "You know." I said I might or I might not, I wasn't sure. I wanted her to tell me. She said, "I'm scared."

I said, "You are scared." It was a declarative. She looked at me and said, "You know that, don't you?" I said I did know it at times, but today? She talked about finishing college and how she might want to be a social worker but was "too crazy." We sat in comfortable silence for 10 minutes and then she left at the end of the hour.

There were no interpretations, no going into what she had shared, as it seemed full in itself. However, after that session I felt that she had an increased capacity to be on her own, and I made it clear that I thought it would be important for her now to begin her session in any way she wanted with whatever came into her mind. She went into an angry silence, and I said that unlike last week when we were comfortable and together, I felt now the silence was full of her anger and demands that I talk.

She spent the next few months beginning sessions with a variety of silent ways ... but predominantly complaining, defiant, or nasty. After the nasty complaints for me to start, she would at times go into a vindictive silence.

One day she came in and plopped on the chair and remained in deadening silence. I felt I could hardly keep my eyes open.

After several months of anger at being left on her own, she began to come up out of the silence in more ways; there was a coming out in confusion, in lightness, humor, tenderness, deadness, meanness, hurt, seriousness, reflectiveness, fear.

It was my observation of her increased participation through her facial gestures that originally led me to feel that for the first time she was able to be more on her own. I went from talking casually at times for 3 months to asking questions, to letting her say more and having silence intermittent with talking, to having her start the session. I believe that if I had not waited for this period and had not talked for so long, she would have been unable to see me. She remembers those early sessions and said, "I couldn't talk when I first came." She never told me why.

At this point, after one year, we can now discuss how she demanded that other people take care of her, for she is now able to see the actuality of her behavior and no longer needs to remain silent. She can now choose either to talk or not talk. She had to be stronger before this could happen. I *saw* her fear when treatment began and it led me to correct action, *letting her be* to heal in her way in our relationship. We now explore her use of silence as a means of avoiding anxiety at times, and now it has meaning for her. She was not able to do this before our year of work in which I gave her the space to enter the world with me, in her own way at her own pace.

This treatment is unorthodox. However, throughout this work I was trusting my inner experience of how to proceed and had few concepts to go by. I was thus working intuitively, aware that my central focus was to meet the patient's need.

1.9 Healing Occurs When We are Not Talking About an Inner Feeling or Thought but are Being It

Some of the most powerful healing moments in psychotherapy come when the patient finds the way out of suffering. He learns that the liberation from suffering is suffering itself such that there is no separation, so that at the moment of genuine suffering there is no experience of a "sufferer." He discovers that the way out of sorrow is being the sorrow, for when he is fully the sorrow there is no "he" consciousness at all. There is only sorrow. Being this sorrow there is no thought, no commentary, no separation. One is then totally tears and aches and sobs. One is not thinking how awful the sorrow is when one is being it. A cry, "oooh," is radically different from "Why am I sad? In being sorrow one is released from this into a new feeling state.

1.9.1 Examples of being an inner feeling or thought

Example One: Patient initially came to see me with her fear of an intimate relationship. She has been talking about her mother coming into the bedroom at night
before she would go to sleep. She has described this many times before with an
account of her feelings, her fears of her mother, her mother's tension, the un-
speakable distance between them, her longing to reach her mother, etc. This time
she mentions her mother's being at the door and then she breaks out in sobs,
saying, "Oooh . . . ooh . . . " It is a long, loud deep sound full of pain. She begins
to curl up and scream the same sound. She remains with this for most of the
session. She then tells me that she is afraid very afraid. Crying and smiling, she
then says I am so grateful to you and to myself and I'm so glad to be alive."
She looked quite peaceful for the first time since I had seen her. She then said,
"The sky outside your window is so blue, and so clear . . . "

Example Two: Pt: I had a long talk with Susan, and as we were talking I saw that she
doesn't care for me. It's very hard to look at. I can let it in now how she doesn't
love me. And when we were talking I could feel how much I care . . . and afraid to
let myself go. . . . And now I just feel . . . it hurt like hell. I'm furious with myself
that I love someone who doesn't love me. It's . . . all the words can't make it
different. (silence)

Patient lies quietly for about 20 minutes and is breathing very heavily with a
slight trembling in the limbs. I then say that we have to end for now and he looks
intensely at me, saying nothing. I feel his intense hurting in all of this, and feel his
inner strength in seeing the hurt, being the hurting inside.

**Being who you are or being the experience does not mean you feel no
pain,** but that you are not thinking it is no good. When you are not
fighting it but being it, it will fade away and other inner events will
emerge.

2.0 Healing Occurs When We Let Go of Concepts and Move into Silence Awareness in Which We are the Fullness We are Seeking

There are times when we see that words or thoughts can't solve our
problems. Then we let go into our inner silence. After the silence, we
sometimes say it was a time of great inner peace.

2.0.1 Example of letting go into Silence Awareness

A patient has been talking for months about trying to get work as an actress. She has
been over her feelings about it, her ideas on how come she can't find work. She has
been through a lot of inner turmoil wondering if this is the right work for her. She
is clearly exhausted from her self denigration at not finding work. She comes in one
day and says.

Pt: I have no urge to talk. There doesn't seem to be anything left to say. (silence for
     25 minutes   then patient begins to cry softly, then smiles) I have nothing in
     my mind for once. This feels like the first time I let go altogether here. I wasn't
     having any thoughts. I feel very good.
Patient begins the next session saying:
Pt: I had a profound experience last time. I just let myself be and I felt good. I
     think there's a lot for me to learn from that. I realized after that if I could leave myself
     alone not keep thinking or figuring things out I could be fine.
Th: You are fine.
Pt: I know. But I forget it. (laughing)

2.1 Holistic Change Occurs When We Have an Insight into the Limited Value of Some of Our Thoughts and How We Cling to Them

2.1.1 Examples of insight into some of our thoughts

Example One: Pt: I was home this weekend without any plans and without any
     dates. You know there's no one in my life right now. I kept thinking how I'm
     without anyone, and over and over, how this has been going on for a while . . .
     and thinking of all my friends who have somebody and what I do wrong, and
     how I'm not pretty. Then I started thinking how I'd be alone for the rest of
     time, always on the outside of life, never a part of the action. And I got very sad
     . . . and of course I started drinking and went to bed and was crying. Then I
     went to sleep. I was completely miserable. I was exhausted from my own
     thoughts of how no one loves me.
          There's this thing that happens, and I can watch it. I watch myself going into
     this funk, and exactly what I think, and to me my worst enemy are these
     thoughts. I do want to talk to someone, to hold someone and all that. But I
     can live with that   . . it's the thoughts that do me in. And I lose control . . . I
     give into them like I'm in a psychic bloodbath until I'm either drunk or crying
     and feeling hopeless. I see that I hang onto these ideas as if they have something
     good to give me or teach me but it's always the same thing . . . being miserable.
     How come I give them so much power . . . or even go over them all the time?
     And I can see when it's going to begin . . . I watch the spiral start but I'm not
     sure how to stop it. No, it's that I don't want to stop it. I let the thoughts take
     over. What good do they do me? If I was going to go out, by the time I'm into
     these thoughts I have no hope of doing anything.
Th: So that you cling to these thoughts that create your misery. What would happen
     if you didn't give them so much power . . . just let them come and go . . . would
     other thoughts come?
Pt: Yes. Like this weekend I thought, none of this is true. You are a perfectly
     attractive woman and you hung onto Jack for years for fear that no one would
     like you . . but I did see for a moment that all this negative stuff is only a part
     of the picture.
Th: Only thoughts . . . and a small part of the whole of your thoughts. What do you
     feel is the larger whole?
Pt: It would be something about how I'm a good person, and attractive, and really
     quite wonderful . . (silence), and that I would have to make some effort to get

out and meet people.

Th. You cling to certain thoughts and they have limited value. They create suffering. And you can let them go, and see that they are only thoughts. Even if they came you wouldn't have to give them so much value. You already see the limited value they have to create what you want in living.

Pt: I can see that this is what keeps me in this patern of withdrawal and drinking on the weekend. So maybe I can have the thoughts and just not let them take me over. I will have to remember that they are only thoughts. It's like watching them, and not letting them flatten me . . . not letting them control me. I could stop the spiral if I watched. I will try to do this.

Example Two: Pt: I always think I'm angry. I see myself as an angry person. Most of the time I'm thinking it I'm not even angry. But it's like a constant reminder not to get angry. More than that, when I'm actually angry it's horrible, but then it goes away, but this thought just stays. Sometimes I think that it even shows on my face when I think it. I think how nobody wants an angry person around, or I think what if they knew I was so angry, and how I can explode. I think it so much it's like I convince myself, and then I think I am an angry person, but I'm angry as much as I think it, and the thoughts hold me back a lot from feeling just relaxed in the way I am with people.

Th: This thought has a powerful hold on you. Can you see how it is only a thought and that it isn't disappearing maybe since you're insisting on holding onto it?

Pt: I am an angry person, and resentful. This is who I am.

Th: Yes, when you are angry you are angry. But all the times in between it's just a thought. It's not the anger. Anyway, you don't know all the other ways you could be since you're so busy thinking you're angry. This thought keeps you from finding out the other ways you are. What contact have you had with some of these other ways?

Pt: You mean like nice, and funny?

Th: And . . . ?

Pt: (laughing) I see what you mean. Well, when I'm angry I'm angry, but as you say all the times in between (laughing) . . . I fill in with this thought. I was almost trained to see myself this way. I had a terrible temper and my parents would always tell people I was the most angry of their kids . . . I think it and so it is. It's like my head or my thoughts create the world for me. And so when I think all the time I'm this one way I can't ever be any other way. So now it's me, and this way of thinking is what's holding me back, and keeping me locked up inside. Only a thought.

Th: Yes, and only one thought among so many possibilities.

Pt: It's amazing how I've always thought this and imagined it's who I am. "Angry." Well . . . we'll see what happens. That gives me some hope!

2.2   Healing Occurs When We Drop Our Notions of Life And Open Ourselves to Seeing Things as They Are

Therapists have many notions of how patients should behave in the session. Often these concepts have nothing to do with the patient and actually block the patient's opening up with the therapist. Holding onto these notions often traps us so that we cannot learn more of how things are in fact. Notions of how patients are to treat us, act, how therapy is to proceed, how life is to be for us, keep us in resentful inner states when people or circumstances don't match our notions. When we try to match a patient to books or supervisors or previous experience we cannot see that patient. Similarly, we can never meet the needs of a patient when we have a notion of how he is to behave in therapy which is radically different than how he does behave.

In the example below, the therapist is angry with the patient's way of coming to the first three sessions with food. He has a notion that this is not *the way* in therapy. He has tried to link it with the patient's wanting to avoid, breaking rules, etc., but has gotten no place. He then lets go of this and opens himself to finding out what the patient might be expressing.

2.2.1 Example of seeing things as they are

Pt: Hi.

Th. Hi.

Pt: What's up?

Th: Not much. How about you?

Pt: Things are okay with me.

(Patient is carrying a bag which he now opens. In it is a paper-wrapped hamburger on which he puts ketchup from a plastic container, then takes salt out of another container . . . spilling some on the floor . . . saying I'm sorry . . . doesn't clean it up. He then takes out a bag of french fries, and then a coke on which he opens the lid. The therapist is silent.)

Pt: They didn't give me onions . . . shit. (Patient begins to eat) I don't care for hamburgers without onion, do you?

Th: I like onions.

Pt: I would return this . . . only I'm here now . . . I dropped salt on the floor. (reaches for a Kleenex to pick it up) It's already in the rug . . . do you mind?

Th: I don't care for salt on the rug . . .

Pt: I mean do you really mind?

Th: I would say I'm affected but not upset.

Pt: (begins eating and eats in silence for a few moments) Would you like some? (offering french fries)

Th: No thanks.

Pt: Do you mind if I eat?

Th: No. Do you?

Pt: What?

Th: Mind eating in front of me?

Pt: You mean I'm a slob?

Th: Are you being a slob as you experience it?

Pt: I eat fast like I'm starving to death . . . Ann says I'm a slob. Did you notice me eating?

Th: Well, I'm in the room. Of course I noticed it.

Pt: How do I look eating . . . like I never ate a meal before. Ann says it makes her sick to watch me eat. Now I'm starting to feel like you think I'm eating like I have no manners, which is true. I thought of coming here and eating, and I didn't like it, but I'm hungry. This is the time I eat dinner.

Th: Uh-huh.

Pt: Are you watching me?

Th: Yes.

Pt: Do I look funny eating?

Th: You don't look funny, but you do eat fast. Maybe here you want to get it over. It's going pretty fast.

Pt: Everything with me is rush. I got so much to do . . . and I wanted to tell you to clean up the salt. I could do a better job with the salt, then I thought, fuck it . . . (eating in silence). In a way I'm glad you get to see me eating . . . it's embarrassing. . . . I feel embarrassed, like I eat and spill . . . I rush even when I talk, even when I pee. I can't just do something . . . I'm thinking of the next thing, like now I'm rushing to eat so I can put all the papers in the bag, and then you won't notice me, and I won't. It's sort of being afraid and feeling ashamed. I feel ashamed a lot, and I'm convinced I'm eating like I have no manners . . . I wonder if I just left the salt, then what . . .

Th: We could see.

Pt: Leave it?

Th: (silent)

Pt: I have to take my direction from you.

Th: What is it you want to do?

Pt: (taking a deep breath . . . and then laughing a little) I want to come in and eat and laugh and spill all over and have fun.

Th: (silent)

Pt: I forgot how ashamed I am . . . I know I'm supposed to come in here and talk all this over . . . (reaching into bag) I brought you some coffee.

Th: I don't want any coffee. Thanks though.

Pt: Great.

Th: What's great?

Pt: That you can tell me to get lost.

Th: I said that?

Pt: I don't know. It felt that way.

Th: I don't want the same thing as you and that's telling you get lost?

Pt: I feel that way. I feel I did something wrong. (bending down to pick up the salt with a Kleenex he has taken from the table). Do you save the salt?

Th: No I can let things go . . . what about you?

Pt: (laughing) I save everything. I save every gesture and remember. I'm making a case that you don't like me, or that you think this is not the way to come to therapy, or that I shouldn't eat here or I eat wrong, or that I'm trying to buy you off with this coffee.

  I actually feel that you made me clean this up, but you didn't – I feel you did. I know I have contempt for myself for spilling a little salt . . . but that is how I am. I do things that are not expected and then I insist on this, and I end up feeling I did the wrong thing. But I do it. Actually I'm glad you got to see me this way in a way, although it's embarrassing. (silent)

Th: Did you feel I didn't want you to eat here?

Pt: I did before tonight. But tonight you seemed more relaxed with it. I thought it
     pissed you before 'cause you made some type of remarks about it. But you were
     looser tonight. I feel very weird . . . (starting to cry a bit). If you are nice to me
     . . . a bit . . . like tonight, then I feel scared . . . Well, there doesn't seem to be
     much to say. I think I told you a lot about myself. I mean my feelings were a
     little hurt when you said I ate "fast" even when I told you that I ate fast. I guess
     . . . I want to tell you that I feel scared.
Th: Are you scared of me when I am nice?
Pt: Yes, very. I feel this terrific urge to just be quiet. (He cleans up all the stuff that
     is on the table from the paper bag. He takes the napkin and wipes up the crumbs
     and removes more salt from the floor. He then goes on to talk about how it is
     having to do the unexpected and says he feels afraid of this.)

As the therapist is able to drop his notions of how the patient should
behave, the patient is freer to reveal more of who he is and thus is more.
Both people are describing ideas they have clung to, and are beginning to
open up to how things are in actuality.

Holistic change occurs when we are more aware of how we all share a
common bond of being alive, of being a form in the universe. We begin to
feel into the facades of all people, to feel into the pain, the confusion, the
despair we all live in, and we feel a deep connection with the courage of all
who are in life. We actually enhance another person's being more in life
by participating with them in the wholeness of the present moments we
call the session. It is the nature of the participation with the person we call
the patient that will lead either to continued closure or greater openness in
finding out our potential for living.

There are moments in most every session in which there is a transformation of both patient and therapist. These events signal the awakening of
the healing powers available in a human relationship. In these moments
there is:

1) an awakening of energy

2) a sense of something new happening in the therapeutic encounter

3) a difference from other times. There may be silence, memories,
images, feelings, thoughts, sensations that emerge out of this difference.

4) a more active participation which is a rootedness in this very
moment.

We want to find these moments in the session where there is something
new emerging, some new form of behavior or relating, any incipient
process, less compulsive behavior, more wholeness, a sense of connecting
in a new way in the therapeutic relationship, a new beginning, even in a
new gesture, a subtle nuance in the voice that wasn't there before. These
will be places where we focus with exploring.

The patient enters treatment expecting everything to be done *to* him, deeply feeling that no one could really care to find out who he is, feeling magical in expectations and also feeling hopeless that anything profound can happen from inside of himself, wanting to be involved, not knowing how, not wanting to make effort, wanting to. The therapist earns the trust necessary to go on by being consistently empathic, open, able to bear the weight of the feelings that emerge in the patient without needing to escape from this.

There are moments of unity in psychotherapy where the patient and therapist are working together where their roles are dropped and there is a felt sense of being involved in participating, forgetting time, being *in* the moment. Duality at such moments has ceased. In such moments of unity of being, there is a way of being together which creates increased energy in both parties and which lends strength to both parties for something real has been shared which cannot be erased. In all of the examples given there is this sense of unity.

Out of this unity, healing occurs. Out of the unity, there emerges a greater sense of differentiation, a relaxation of images in favor of inquiry into phenomena as they occur. Out of a sense of knowing that there is another person with whom we can share our deepest feelings, we find the strength to look at *what is* and to see the actuality of how we live, who we are. When we can see what is more clearly, this *in-sight* has reverberations and meaning. New actions which are more integral, more whole, come out of the clarity of knowing who we are and how we live in actuality.

Technique is the process of recognizing the moment of participation and experiencing when it occurs. Technique is finding ways to encourage the unfolding of such moments of participation with each patient. At such moments there is the sense of the intrinsic nature of the two people, in which things are as they are, delivered from the strain of having to be any particular way. Here the therapist feels the meaning of the contact without having any desire to hold onto it; making no effort for it, he finds it. Here there is nothing to be analyzed, to be explained, to be sought. *When two people have experiences of such events together, there is the creation of new energy in which healing occurs. At such moments there is no longer a fear of not getting something or other. There is no proving who one is. There is the wonder of being alive in which one is the wholeness one is seeking, and one is sufficient.*

Holistic change occurs in the mutual action of participating together. In a session a patient has been talking of people not liking her, but it is clear in observing her that she is feeling some liking for herself:

Pt: Do you like me?
Th: (feeling liking) A feeling is coming up in me now of liking you.
Pt: I don't feel sure that you can.
Th: (who at that moment feels caring but says nothing, knowing the feeling is sufficient)
Pt: Do you . . . (sighs)
     (Therapist breathes deeply for several seconds. Then the patient talks of something related to liking. There is a feeling of comfort in being together.)

Here there is the action of participation together and a moment of healing where the patient can feel the caring, doesn't dwell on it, but observably absorbs the therapist's caring.

Here in this clinical example is a beginning awareness of how it is outside the perpetual battlefields of daily life where something else is always wanted, where happiness is fleeting, where comparing is continual. Here the patient and therapist feel complete. In this brief example, there is a beginning feeling of some of what we can find in psychotherapy. I would put it this way:

You are one with what you are telling, feeling, seeing . . . there is no separation between what is seen and the seer . . . one is whole . . . wholly participating in what is taking place. One is living in the moment, one is complete being who one is. At such times one is changing, one is whole.

Liberation from psychological illness happens in getting rooted in experiencing the self, others, and the world in this very moment. To know myself as I am I have to be it. To know life is to appreciate that all we have is this very moment. Psychotherapy is a process where we come to know who we are in the very moment of being.

References

1. Lao Tzu, *The Way of Life*, trans. Witter Bynner (New York: Capricorn Books, 1962), p. 25.
2. D. W. Winnicott, "The Capacity to be Alone," *The Maturational Processes and the Facilitating Environment* (New York: International Universities Press, 1965), pp. 29-37.
3. Harry Stack Sullivan, *The Interpersonal Theory of Psychiatry* (New York: W. W. Norton & Company, 1953), p. 110.